ALL IN YOUR HEAD

What Happens When Your Doctor Doesn't Believe You?

Marcus Sedgwick

HAWKSMOOR
PUBLISHING

First published in 2022 by Hawksmoor Publishing,
an imprint of Bennion Kearny Limited.

Woodside, Oakamoor, ST10 3AE, UK

www.hawksmoorpublishing.com

ISBN: 978-1-914066-21-4

Variable, and therefore miserable condition of man! this minute I was well, and am ill, this minute. I am surprised with a sudden change, and alteration to worse, and can impute it to no cause, nor call it by any name.

John Donne
– Devotions Upon Emergent Occasions,
and severall steps in my Sicknes, 1624

Preface

I had written three, maybe four drafts of this book, when seemingly overnight, the world was turned upside down. It was forced to stay at home, locked down, locked *in*, for fear of some largely unknown and terrifying illness. An unseen beast was stalking our streets, workplaces and playgrounds, and as the world – some of it sooner, some of it later – started to realise that this was not a matter that could be easily predicted, or ignored, or simply brazened out, it was forced into the state we came to call confinement. But this monumental, global cataclysm was something strangely familiar to great numbers of people. In fact, for some millions of people around the world, the state of being largely or entirely confined at home, and the state of suffering from a poorly understood disease was, already, their daily existence.

I am one of those people.

I became one of those people seven years ago, with the arrival in my life of an unwanted stranger, though this stranger was someone who was also very familiar. It was me; to be precise, a sick version of me. As I write, I've only been ill for seven years, but that seven years has been enough to establish that the cause of my illness cannot be established. I remained undiagnosed. For those who might say that comparison with the pandemic should not be made, since this undiagnosed illness of mine is not life-threatening, I would just ask you to read on, because there are one or two things to say about that. And though, at first, they might appear to be very different sicknesses, there is a relationship between them of which many people are only just becoming aware. Just like confinement, this is an illness that locks you in with yourself; it forces you to confront your deepest, truest self; there are no more distractions of work, or friends, or hobbies.

Whatever it was you used to do that defined you may have been taken from you. There is just you, and four walls, something that most of us never had to contemplate. Until the cataclysm came along and changed all that.

But more plainly: in March of 2020, as the pandemic really took hold, I wrote to a number of national newspapers in the UK and the US, offering them a story I felt they might want to run. In the story, I predicted the arrival of the thing we now call Long Covid, though I didn't use that phrase, for it hadn't been coined yet. This wasn't such an extraordinary piece of fortune-telling – there were dozens of us crying the same warning, dozens of people like me, for whom an acute, viral infection had been the trigger for something much more permanent. From our perspective, it was easy to see that the relatively small number of people with a lifelong illness would soon become a huge number. This was the story I offered to the papers – none of them were interested. As Cassandra of Troy found to her cost, you cannot tell people what to be interested in, until it is too late.

But this is what the pandemic has already started to do. It has turned a minority health issue into a global concern. Not the matter of the acute illness, as frightening as that might be, but the long-form sickness that can follow – for many people who contract the Coronavirus, for those who do not make a total recovery, the world will never be the same again. What was a story that affected perhaps less than 1% of the world population is becoming a story that everyone will be familiar with. It will happen to someone you know; it will happen to someone you work with, someone in your family, someone you love. It might even happen to you.

This book isn't a story, not exactly. Neither is (my) illness a story, but through writing this book and in being ill, I was brought face to face with the role that stories play in our lives; the way we each tell 'our story', and what happens when that story breaks down. When it no longer works. When meaning can no longer be applied. Something that has now also been replicated on a worldwide scale, as we have seen the near shattering of a myth that I would suggest most people in the world still hold to be true, still *need* to be true: that we are in charge of the world, and not the other way around.

This book is about the stories we tell, which ones we want to hear, and which we don't. It's about seven years in a life, in which I tried to work out what was wrong with me when no doctor could; the effect that had on my personal narrative; and more than anything else, the damage done to you when your doctor does not believe you. This, too, might happen to you.

1 – The Nervy Ones

'Now, tell me,' she said, in a deliberate stage whisper, leaning across me to get closer to the centre director, with whom we had been discussing some practical matters ahead of a week's writing retreat. 'Tell me, who are the ones with food issues? Because I usually find those are the nervy ones.'

'She' was one of the senior figures of writing for children in the UK from the last forty years, one of those women sometimes still referred to as a 'grande dame' of that world. We were sitting with the director, who I'll call Mary because that's her name, on a picnic bench in the garden of the house where the retreat was to take place. It was May, Monday afternoon, sunny and more than warm. The house was old, very old, as remote as you can get in England, with no phone reception, and not another house or building of any kind to be seen within the horizon. A shallow bowl of English farmland and woods, holding the long, low, thatched manor house, dated at a thousand years old, at least. It's a special place.

We were having the usual meeting before the arrival of the student writers, to fine-tune how our week would go. I had never worked with the Grande Dame before; in fact, we had only just met.

'Food Issues.'

'The Nervy Ones.'

I could hear her capitalising the words as she spoke, and she spoke with such an air of knowing, of superiority, of imparting sage wisdom and insight that she and only she had finessed out of the mess of human experience, that I felt there was but one response. Mary seemed to be hesitating, and was it my imagination or did I sense she was also a little taken aback by this statement?

So I put my hand up like the naughty schoolboy I was admitting to being.

'Uh, that'll be me.'

As I spoke, I realised that Mary had sheets of paper in front of her, one of which listed the various allergies and intolerances of everyone present for the week. Including the tutors. So she would have known about my intolerance of gluten, of coffee. She would probably have remembered that bringing a red pepper or a chilli into close proximity with me would cause a severe allergic reaction. So perhaps I was right; she had been hesitating, wondering how to answer the GD, without insulting me.

I was rather surprised at myself. I'm not often so bold. Especially with two strangers, for I had only just met Mary too. But good. I got a laugh from both of them and congratulated myself for diffusing any awkwardness, since everyone knows that if there's anything that three nicely-brought-up Britons cannot abide, it's awkwardness.

We glossed over the topic and moved on, but I had already made a bigoted decision – that I did not especially like the Grande Dame. As the week went on, though, I realised that, as so often, first impressions can be wrong, and that was true in this case. In fact, I came to realise that the GD was not just unlikeable, but utterly insufferable. And it seemed not just to me, but even to the writers who'd come on the retreat, one of whom refused the scheduled second tutorial with her, something I had never come across in ten years of teaching, on the grounds that she had been unnecessarily patronised in the first. Yet, as is almost always the case when someone says something that riles you, it's because you suspect there may be a grain of truth in it.

Food Issues, The Nervy Ones.

Did she, although I hated to admit it, have a point? I thought back across all the retreats I'd taught, I thought about other friends and acquaintances, and tried in an utterly anecdotal, unscientific way to see if it were generally true that it was 'nervy' people who were the ones with food 'issues', an expression I detest in itself. It's not an 'issue' that someone with a peanut allergy may die from merely touching the armrest on an airplane where someone was previously wiping their sticky paws; it's a fact. A really crappy fact.

But, I wondered, is there a link between problems with certain foods and nervous dispositions? Was my gut feeling that the sensitive guts of sensitive people, and their personalities, are in some way connected correct? In short, was the Grande Dame right?

I didn't yet reach a conclusion with my unscientific ponderings, but she had planted the seed of a thought. Or, to be more precise, she had watered a seed that had already been planted, a year or so earlier, just after I became ill. That seed had been planted by someone else – a doctor, in fact.

More of that in a moment. For now, I went on with the week as best I could. By a chance conversation, I found that one of the writers who'd come on the retreat also had Chronic Fatigue Syndrome, or CFS, also known as ME,* which is what I had been told was wrong with me. She asked me how long I had been ill.

'Around fifteen months,' I told her. 'No, hang on, sixteen.'

She told me she had been ill for thirteen years.

At that time, I found that intolerably depressing. Thirteen years. Thirteen. Years. I was struck by the strength with which she told me this, without falling to pieces, as I felt I was at the time, something I was trying to keep hidden from everyone. She

---

* What is ME, or CFS? This book is not intended to be solely about the illness I have, rather it's about what happens when you fall ill with any poorly understood malady and are not taken seriously by your doctor. For that reason, and because it's no simple matter to explain, I have placed a brief description of the disease as the appendix to the book. But, be warned, 'it's complicated'.

explained how she'd been really bad for the first year or so, confined to bed in a darkened room, unable to bear neither light nor sound. She told me about all the treatments she had tried, physiological approaches as well as psychological ones. She told me how she had made some breakthroughs over the years, and had improved a lot, to the point where she was now well enough to come on a writing retreat, or walk her dog a couple of times a week when back home. Which was encouraging, or should have been, but back then, a year and a bit into being ill, the thought of thirteen years was almost too much to bear. But then, maybe I'm only saying that because I am one of those nervy ones, a pathetically sensitive soul.

*

It hadn't helped that in those first months of being ill, I'd had a succession of people sharing their stories about CFS, also commonly still known by the earlier name of myalgic encephalomyelitis, or ME, now sometimes also known as SEID; Systemic Exertion Intolerance Disorder.*

My mind and my body were occupied with being terrified. I'd been trying to go on working, though it was hard. I wasn't writing; there was no book 'on the go' as they say, and that was probably

---

* The mere existence of an array of acronyms should have been a major clue, when I first became ill, that no one really yet knows what's going on with this illness. I should also point out that even the names we use for this illness can be the source of argument, bitterness and recrimination; even – I was dismayed to find out – among the society of people who are suffering from it. I tend to avoid these arguments, and in this book I will use the names interchangeably, as well as my own preferred term; undiagnosis. This is not a book about ME/CFS specifically; it's a book about having a poorly understood illness and not having your doctors take you seriously. The appendix to the book explains a little more of the controversy around the merely very name of this disease.

just as well, since I was finding it hard to think straight, to find words. I would often break off in the middle of a sentence, invert two words in a sentence, or just not be able to think of the word I wanted at all, sometimes even very basic ones. For someone who makes a living through putting words together, what was happening to my mind was pretty scary, but at the time, I was more worried about what had happened to my body, more or less overnight. One day I had been well, as fit as I had ever been since childhood. Almost the next, I was confined to life in bed or at best on the sofa; some days, it was a major achievement to walk from one end of my tiny house to the other. And yet I kept on pushing; kept trying to work.

As well as the writing itself, I also used to give talks in schools and other places about writing, and I had continued with the bookings I had already agreed to. It wasn't something I relished doing, though I'd become quite good at it, and sometimes even really enjoyed talking about books and writing with young adventurous minds, minds often overlooked and patronised, I felt. But, the thing was, I'd never lost sight of the cosmic joke that, on the day I left school at the age of 18, I swore I would never step foot in a school again as long as I lived. School had not suited me (nor I it, I suspect), and the whole thing had been torment for someone like me; which is to say, someone *nervy*.

School. Even the very word is ugly to me. So the fact that now, as an adult, month in, month out, I would pitch up at the gates of some comprehensive in Swansea, Wales, or some private joint in Massachusetts, USA, swallow all the horrors that had befallen me at my own educational establishment, and go through it all again was not something I ever really got over. Visiting all-boys' schools was the worst; I used to joke with myself about flashbacks as if I was some war vet with PTSD (and only much later came to understand this is closer to the truth than I had thought possible), I used to tell myself it might even be good for me, and, if all those self-help books and advice gurus are to be believed, perhaps it could be cathartically therapeutic. I wrestled with what the powers-that-were said at my Grammar school about every instance of abuse, physical and mental, that was inflicted upon us; namely that it was 'character building'. Every foul torture, every knee in the groin, every knife waved around in the playground, every dirty sexual innuendo from boy or teacher, every moment of nasty, belittling threat, yes, they were all character building; it's just that the characters they built in that school were mostly deeply fucked-up neurotic young men. Even some of the bullies went on to kill themselves, I heard by chance, decades later. *Even?* Maybe I don't mean 'even'.

But I went on surrendering to the cosmic joke, and turned up as usual at a series of schools that spring, with a pretence of confidence and a bunch of stories to tell about how much fun it is being a writer, some of them even true. Because much of the weakness brought by my illness is in my legs, I had been forced to ask the organiser for a stool or chair to sit on while I spoke. Even that was a mental hurdle for me to pass – I hated having to admit I was ill, more to myself than anyone else, I now realise; hated having to discuss it; hated having to explain why a tall, apparently healthy-looking 45-year-old man couldn't stand for more than five minutes, but I had to, and I did.

And when I did, people would share their stories of Chronic Fatigue Syndrome. The first thing that struck me is that almost everyone seemed to know someone who had it, or had had it. A cousin, a sister, a daughter, an uncle, a workmate... Before it happened to me, I had heard of ME, but I didn't really know what it was. I knew it was sometimes passed off as 'yuppie flu' or just called being 'tired all the time', but I had no real knowledge of it, and it would also be accurate to say I had no idea how little knowledge anyone else has about it either. By whom, I mean doctors. But here it was; everyone, it seems, knows someone with it, and I was struck by the thought of a massive, unexplored, rarely discussed epidemic of sickness. (This was six years before a 'real' epidemic came along, a pandemic in fact, and by real, I mean one which *all* doctors agree exists.) In the UK, it's estimated that at least 250,000 people are sufferers. In the US, at least a million. Worldwide, estimates range from 17 to 24 million.[i]

24 million out of approaching 8 billion people gives us a figure of 0.3% of the world population. That's to speak only about ME/CFS, but even if we throw in the many similar misunderstood conditions – POTS, MCAS, MCS, etc, – we will still only arrive at a tiny proportion of the human species. Yet, as I said in the introduction to this book, this will change. It already is. You will already know someone struggling with 'Long Covid'*; perhaps you already know someone who's been told what I was about to be told by my doctor about my mysterious illness…

*

As people shared these stories, another thing stuck out; they would without fail be sure to tell me how long the person they knew with CFS had been ill. I started to play a morbid little game with myself; keeping a mental count of the years, waiting for someone to outdo the current highest total. Two years. Five. Six. Any advance on six? Yes! Eight! Nine. *Thirteen.* Then, someone in a school I have forgotten told me about an ex-colleague who'd had it for thirty years.

---

* This is not to say that Long Covid is necessarily the same as ME/CFS. As I write these matters are being fiercely debated, and it may well be that Long Covid is not ME/CFS. It may also be the case, that there is a 'Long Covid' illness, as well as a distinct number of people who have ME/CFS triggered by Covid. A well-balanced article on this is here: https://www.nytimes.com/2021/01/21/magazine/covid-aftereffects.html

Thirty years. Game over, I thought. How could you be ill for thirty years, I wondered? And of course, what I suppose I really meant by that was, how can you *bear* to be ill for thirty years? I pushed the thought away as much as I could, but I failed.

As these kinds of conversations multiplied, as everyone casually dropped years at me like a judge handing out sentences, I wondered what was going on. Was it like a report card, or some badge of honour? Did they think telling me would help? I know no one meant any of it unkindly, but back then I was still hoping that if my illness might no longer be measured in weeks, I might perhaps be able to keep it to months, and not years. And every story depressed me a little more.

Then, in a beautiful school in Sussex in the South of England, someone found a way to beat the lot. She won the game, hands down.

'Oh, yes,' said the friendly librarian who had invited me to speak. 'Yes, ME. It's terrible. I read about a girl in the local paper. Only eighteen. She killed herself.'

Suicide. Now that's a genuine life sentence.

'Oh,' I said. 'Um. Yes. Shall we check the projector is working?'

*

But this conversation about killing yourself was yet to come that May morning as Mary and I were being told how nervy people are the ones prone to having 'issues about food', with the clearly stated additional 'fact' that most of them use it as an attention-seeking device.

'Not intentionally, of course,' the GD said, looking at me pointedly. 'Well, not always. And, of course, there are some people who really do have problems. Coeliacs, for example. Are you coeliac?'

'No,' I said, feeling inadequate for not being sufficiently ill. 'No, it's just an intolerance. It's weird though; it just came on, last year when I got –'

'My niece is coeliac. Terribly hard. Terribly. It's getting easier to find things in the supermarkets now, but in restaurants, well, you can never take the risk.'

So we chatted on and Mary smoothed the conversation deftly in a different direction, and the week passed, and we helped the writers on the retreat take a step or two to wherever it was they wanted to go, and I pondered more about whether this illness of mine was real.

For that had been the seed, the original seed that had been planted by the very first doctor I saw when I got back from Asia, with stiff muscles and painful joints, with earache and dizziness, with fever and aching bones, with diarrhoea and trembling hands, and above all, an unrelenting, dreadful exhaustion, as if every cell in my body had simply given up or broken down.

*

My usual, excellent GP, who I'll call Dr Beattie because that was her name, was on sabbatical. In her place was a medical student from the University Hospital. She would not yet be qualified for another year or so, but I had no prejudice about that. She had the nurse take some blood and ordered some routine tests. A few days later, I returned to get the results. They'd found nothing in any of them – all negative.

This was a few weeks into being ill. At this point, I had great difficulty walking even a few steps; my legs seemed to have seized up as if they were rusting metal; they felt heavy and throbbed almost all the time. I still had the earache and diarrhoea though some of the initial acute symptoms, such as the aching bones, had eased a little.

She turned away from her computer screen and regarded me, hesitating for a moment. Then, she leaned towards me, fractionally.

'What would you say,' she said, 'if I told you there was nothing wrong with you?'

I didn't say anything at first, I think. I remember not really understanding the question. There clearly was something wrong with me. She must have seen I was confused, because she clarified.

'What would you say if I told you this is all in your head?'

All in your head. There it was. It's not real. You're not necessarily lying; you may not actually be making it up, but you only *think* you're ill. There is nothing wrong with you, not really. Though I didn't know it, with those words, I became condemned to years of something for which I was utterly unprepared, something that became as hard to bear as the physical symptoms of the illness itself.

*

As the months of my illness did indeed start to become years, I came to realise how much this first impression had left on me; how much of an extra burden it was that that very first doctor didn't believe I was ill. Not really. Not *properly* ill, in some fashion. And underneath it was lurking a related idea, that this illness was, in some other fashion, my own fault. As the years went on, it was something I had to find a way through, and just like the Grande Dame and her nervy ones, if I was really honest, it bothered me all the more because a part of me wondered whether it could just be true. That I wasn't really ill. That it really was somehow imaginary, something psychosomatically generated.

I also came to find out that this experience, or some version of it, has happened, *is happening*, to countless numbers of patients across the UK, the US and elsewhere, even before Long Covid, as a lack of diagnosis is quickly transformed into something quite different – the supposition that there must therefore be nothing 'really' wrong with you, not in your body anyway. So that is what this book is about: what happens when your doctor tells you that your illness is 'all in your head.'

It's about where those four words would take me over the next seven years, and are still taking me. It's about what happens when your doctor doesn't believe that you're actually ill; when they doubt the veracity of your lived experience. It's about the strange places you end up when you reach desperation point; the bizarre therapies and sometimes even more bizarre therapists. It's about the crisis of trust that is brewing between patient and their doctor; a process that was well underway before the pandemic, though unseen by most of the world. It's about the hidden reasons why your doctor might be motivated to tell you your illness is psychogenic, which have less to do with medicine and more to do with money. Because as I dug deeper into the stories surrounding unexplained illnesses, I saw behind the veil. Maybe the better metaphor would be that I saw behind the curtain around the hospital bed, and discovered that what is occurring between doctor and patient behind it is not always as positive, hopeful and as based in good science as we might imagine. And finally, it's about the process of trying to find answers, of finding meaning, and what happens when you can't.

This book is not a self-help book. Nor is it a book specifically about the illness known as ME or CFS. In telling my story am trying to bear witness to the state of being maltreated by your doctor through disbelief, whatever the sickness. It will be a story recognised in some form or other by many people, and though it is not a self-help book, I wish I had been armed with some of the facts, arguments and ethics I stumbled across over the years when I set out on the journey – I might have been better prepared. As it was, I could only follow the steps defined by who I was then, what clues I thought it might be wise to investigate.

One avenue I quickly set off down was related to the fact that I am a writer. I use my imagination to create stories. If they're good enough, people buy them. If not, not. It's important, therefore, that I listen to, protect, revere my imagination if I am to continue. In short, I am one of the people that other people call a 'creative type.'

Now, everyone knows it's true that 'creative types' are more prone to mental health problems – to depression, to more extreme forms of mental imbalance. Everyone knows it, and I thought I did too; it's the stuff of popular legend; the tortured poet in the garret, Van Gogh and his ear, Plath and her oven, Woolf with her pockets of stones and the River Ouse beckoning. Book after book and biography after biography asserts the link between creativity and mental un-health. Here's just one account of many to be found in popular non-fiction: "In psychiatrist Arnold Ludwig's massive study of mental illness and creativity, *The Price of Greatness,* he found an 87 per cent rate of psychiatric disorders in eminent poets and a 77 per cent rate in eminent fiction writers – far higher than the rates he found among high achievers in non-artistic fields."[ii]

Since writers and creative types, in general, are more prone to mental illness, perhaps they're also more likely to be psychosomatically ill too? That was the thought that had entered my mind. Had this thought also crossed Dr T's mind? She knew I was a writer; was it simply that and a history of depression that had enabled her to jump to her conclusion?

And then again, I started to wonder, could it also be the case that writers are more *physically* ill as well? Maybe it's a double whammy. The cliché of the writer with poor eyesight and ailing health may be a cliché for the reason that most clichés are; that they're true, or at least have some grain of truth underneath them.

And as I said, everyone knows this stuff to be true. Right?

From the same non-fiction book on writers quoted above, "could it be that something about the writer's life – the loneliness, the frustration, the long rambles through the imagination – actually triggers mental illness? Possibly. But studies of the relatives of creative writers reveal an underlying genetic component."

There. It's indisputably true that there is a link between writing and madness, and the only question, as the young and doomed poet John Keats, himself a doctor, wondered, is whether the writer is patient or healer.

Yet as we'll see later, it turns out that the link between madness and creativity is, in fact, not clear-cut. Studies such as the one quoted above have recently been criticised methodologically; there is actually very little compelling research to prove this thing that everyone 'just knows' to be true. Defining madness isn't as easy as one might think, for one thing. It's often hard to state that an individual is mad, for what do you mean by that? Exactly? And what do you mean by 'creative'?

*

This is also a story without an end. Which means it's not a story at all, because a story *has* to have an end. Without one, it's just a series of events without meaning. The attempt to apply meaning to such series, which we call lives, is why stories were invented in the first place; it's why your home is littered with books, as is mine. And, a few years into the illness, as I looked at the piles of books beside the bed, I wondered, *what is it we're looking for in all these pages?* An answer of some kind? Who knows for sure? We may never find such an answer, but that doesn't mean we ought to stop reading. It is undoubtedly better to read than not to read, and undoubtedly better to write than not to write.

Or so I had always thought. Yet I came to question that very idea, something that was shocking to me at first, but something I have been forced to consider nevertheless. I was forced to consider it via the arrival in my life of this unwanted stranger, the sick version of me.

This was all something I would find out later, but back then, in that doctor's surgery in a village outside Cambridge, England, I was just starting out on the different but related journey; that defining illness isn't as easy as you might think it should be, either. It's sometimes hard to get people to believe an individual is ill, and right then, that individual was me. I had never been so ill in my life, and the only thing my doctor could tell me was that it was all in my head.

---

[i] https://me-pedia.org/wiki/
Epidemiology_of_myalgic_encephalomyelitis_and_chronic_fatigue_sy
ndrome
[ii] Jonathan Gottschall, *The Storytelling Animal*, Houghton Mifflin Harcourt, New York, 2012, p93

2 – Malingerers

'Dr T tells me all your tests are negative,' said the senior partner at the surgery.

I'd asked for a second opinion. I now regretted saying that of course I was happy to see an as-yet-unqualified student; no doubt, I told myself, she'd come straight from a lecture on psychosomatic illness; perhaps she'd been swayed by the school of thought that still holds that ME/CFS is an epidemic of hysteria.* So I'd asked to see one of the senior partners at the surgery.

*

The senior partner in question, Dr K, seemed rather bemused that I was in front of him.

'Your tests are negative,' he repeated, staring at his computer screen. He might have been announcing the weather forecast.

'Yes, I know, but I still feel terrible. I can barely walk.'

'Dr T says she tested your leg function. It's normal.'

I didn't wildly agree with this opinion. She'd asked me to lie down on her couch and pushed down on my legs while I tried to lift them, for about three seconds. It didn't seem remotely scientific to me, but she'd been satisfied my legs were fine. I'd tried to tell her that walking was the main problem; that I could stand for a very short period of time, but that I had no stamina; that I

---

* This belief was, if not originated, then certainly cemented by an academic paper of 1970 discussing the famous outbreak at the Royal Free Hospital, London. It was written by two psychiatrists, neither of whom even saw any of the patients, and published fully 15 years after the event. It has been discredited multiple times since, but is still influential. See the appendix for more.

tired almost immediately. But yes, I could move my leg once; and that seemed enough to satisfy her.

I probably shrugged.

'So why do I feel so sick?'

Dr K definitely did shrug, and in return I started to feel angry.

*

When Dr T had asked what I would say if she were to tell me it was all in my head, I'd paused for a moment. I was feeling frustrated, and when frustrated I had a quick temper. I knew it wouldn't help to get cross. Instead, I forced myself to keep calm and answer her. It's probably one of the few times in my life that I have managed to say what I should have said, in the moment. Everyone knows that feeling described as l'esprit de l'escalier – *the wit of the staircase*, when you only think of the cunning retort you should have after you've left the scene of confrontation and are already on the way out of the door, or lying in bed later that night, wide awake and slowly stewing.

More often than not, the big moments of your life occur and pass without fanfare. There is frequently no warning, no sign telling you that something truly significant to the whole course of your life is about to occur. When such moments happen; accidents, deaths, beautiful meetings, there is often a sense of triviality, even of banality, rather than the blood and thunder which you might later append to the fleeting instant.

This moment, of being told my illness was 'all in your head', wasn't so very different. And yet something made me take my time in replying, and when I did, I replied cautiously. Looking back, I think it was the shock of what she'd suggested that made me take a moment before I answered.

'I would say you're not doing the right tests,' I said very carefully. 'Or that the ones you're doing are not good enough.'

She didn't answer.

Now, in these post-pandemic (or do I mean inter-pandemic?) days, there has been a sudden awakening of the realisation in many people that maybe doctors don't always know everything. That there are gaps. And if pressed, even back then, I would probably have acknowledged that doctors can't always know everything. But that was the myth that was running in my head; that for me, at least, there would never be anything wrong that a doctor couldn't explain. Easily.

'You're not doing the right tests,' I said.

And why did she have no answer to that?

Because it was true? Or worse, could it be that the 'right tests' didn't even exist? Or because it would mean admitting something that I would only find out much later, that fully *one half of the time* you visit your doctor, they do not know what is wrong with you.[*] I'll return to that later, but for now, I was faced with a mute doctor.

Whatever her thoughts, I suppose my reply didn't fit with what she believed. What she'd been taught. I'd only just met this young doctor a couple of weeks before. I made a guess at what had happened: before that first consultation, she would have scanned my notes. What she would have seen in the brief glance that time-hurried doctors are allowed would have been a lifelong history of visits to the doctor, mostly not for physical ailments, but for depression and anxiety – it seemed likely to me she had marked me down as a nervy case, a hypochondriac no doubt to boot, and this was the opinion she was sticking to.

'But what about the gluten thing?' I said. 'How can that be in my head?'

She didn't reply to that either.

---

[*] This is fact according to Dr Diane O'Leary, bioethicist, using the latest available figures for the NHS in the UK.

*

I'd been to Asia. I was working in Malaysia, in Kuala Lumpur, for two weeks, giving yet more talks about writing in various international schools. Since Chinese New Year fell in the middle of the trip and schools would be closed, it had been suggested that I take a holiday. I'd never been to Asia, so I thought I may as well make the most of it, and I'd booked myself a little luxury; a long weekend on a Thai island, a cabin overlooking the sea and nothing to do but read and swim, before strolling the short distance to the restaurant on the beach.

After the holiday, I'd taught for a couple more days in KL, then taken the 14-hour flight back to the UK. And already, I felt rough.

I had diarrhoea, but that didn't worry me too much. I have always had a sensitive stomach – if I get ill at all, frequent trips to the bathroom are often the result, and out of politeness to my hosts I had eaten some curries and other dishes that I would not normally have risked. I assumed it would pass off, as would the tiredness from the jet lag.

But they didn't. A week went by, and I kept on trying to work. I tried to go jogging on my usual 5-kilometre route but had to stop after one K and walk groggily home. I looked up how long jet lag can last and reassured myself that it can take a couple of weeks sometimes to fully get over it, and that it can even lead to an upset stomach. But a couple of weeks came and went and I was still ill, still with the bad stomach.

I went to London, to a big annual gathering of writers and publishers at the South Bank, and on the way home, standing in a crowded tube train, I suddenly felt my head swim and I broke out into a sweat. I made it home, feeling terrible. That weekend, we were due to drive to my mother's in North Wales; my daughter and I. Rather than do the sensible thing and cancel, I pressed on. Halfway there, at the wheel, I started to feel very lightheaded, as if

I was about to faint. We got to Wales and I spent most of the weekend on the sofa.

And it was there, one afternoon, as I walked from the sitting room to the dining room that my legs seized up. In one stride, they just stopped working normally, and it was terrifying. I tried to explain it, but no one really understood what I meant. I still haven't found a way to describe how it felt, how it still feels at the worst times; the weakness, the stiffness. I had never felt my legs in this way before, and I was frightened. Frustrated, too, from my lack of inability to express what was going on, but, I later learned, at least I am in good company on that score. Virginia Woolf once lamented how English has all the words you could need to express the thoughts of Hamlet or the tragedy of Lear, yet has no accurate words for the shiver or the headache. Language fails at the leading edge of illness. "Let a sufferer try to describe a pain in his head to a doctor and language at once runs dry."[i]

Woolf was dead right: heavy, weak, rusty, like walking through the waves at the beach, but the waves are made of treacle; all of these I tried, but nothing was precise, nothing captured it, nor how it had come on in an instant. I couldn't seem to make anyone understand.

We drove home on the Sunday, and then I drove from the East of England to the West Country, where I had a whole week of school visits booked, Monday to Friday, in and around Devon.

That evening, I sat at the hotel restaurant by myself, wondering what on Earth was happening. Some bug picked up in Asia, clearly, but it would go. I had no doubt of that. Not then. Maybe I would be better in the morning, and I needed to be, because it can take a lot of energy to keep 400 14-year-olds amused for an hour, and I was going to have to do that six or seven times that week.

On the Monday morning, I even drove as far as the first school; my hands shaking and fumbling as I tried to put coins into a parking meter, my legs threatening to collapse under me at any moment, my head swimming.

I got back in the car, and I drove home to Cambridge and went straight to the doctor, where I was to meet Dr T for the first time.

*

A few weeks later, with all tests negative, the only thing we had discovered at the suggestion of a doctor from the school of Tropical Medicine in London was that I try omitting lactose and gluten from my diet and see if the diarrhoea stopped. It did. Immediately. I started with milk and cheese again, without a problem. I ate some bread; the diarrhoea returned.

'So how is the gluten intolerance all in my head?' I asked Dr T. 'It's never been a problem before.'

No answer.

A different approach. Let's go along with her view and see if that gets me anywhere.

'Very well, if it's all in my head, can you explain why? You can see I have a history of depression, but as it happens right now, I'm the happiest I have ever been in my life. I am writing full-time, which I love. I am running for the first time in years, and I've found that regular exercise is the first thing that's ever kept the depression at bay. I have a wonderful, happy daughter; I love my house, the village where I live. Hell, the day I landed in Malaysia, I even found out that I'd won the biggest book award in the United States that it's possible for me to win. My life has quite literally never been better. Why would I want to be ill now?'

She frowned.

'It would be hard for me to say.'

No, I thought, and bitterness was growing inside me. No, but it isn't hard for you to tell me it's all in my head.

'You were in Thailand?' she ventured.

Hope rose in me that she was going to speak more specifically about particular diseases in particular climes. I knew that there are sometimes emerging illnesses, at first confined to specific islands, that take time to be recognised.

'Did you have any sexual contact?'

'What?'

'Did you have any —'

'No,' I said. 'The only time anyone even touched me was when I had reflexology and a massage.'

'A massage?'

Oh, why did I tell her that?

'Yes, a massage. *Just* a massage. In the spa in the hotel. A *decent* hotel. The reflexology really—'

She wasn't interested in the reflexology, and she wasn't buying the 'just' part of the massage, so I agreed to have screening for AIDS and other STDs despite the fact that I knew they would come back negative, simply to get her to believe that that was not why I was sick. Maybe then we could move on to more specific tests. But more time was wasted waiting for all that to happen, and when it was done, still she wouldn't take me seriously.

*

So I re-put the question to the senior partner. Surely he'll see sense, I thought.

'How is gluten intolerance all in the head?' I said. 'It's the least of my problems, but surely that shows you that something is going on? Something physical, I mean?'

By this point, I had already become the modern irritation of doctors worldwide – I had started to do my own research on the internet. I had, for example, found an academic paper published at the University of Singapore that showed a link between Dengue Fever and subsequent gluten intolerance.

I tried to tell the senior partner about it.

He wasn't interested. Didn't give it a moment's thought. It was as if I had not spoken.

'Look,' I said, and by now I was only just managing to stay calm, 'you might think I'm a hypochondriac [he gave me an eyeless smile and nodded at me slightly at this point], but I don't care. I just want to get well. You haven't tested me for basic things like thyroid function. You haven't even sent me to a specialist in tropical diseases.'

He looked more serious. He paused.

'That's fair enough. We'll do some more tests.'

As I was leaving his office, he added, 'you know, sometimes we just don't know what's wrong with a patient.'

'I understand,' I said. 'I don't have a problem with that.'

But I wasn't brave enough to add that what I did have a problem with was being told I was imagining my illness, or worse, faking it. And if this seems over the top, or paranoid, and though I didn't know it at the time, there are still senior figures in the medical world who refer to ME/CFS patients explicitly as 'malingerers'. Something else I didn't know then was that this illness has become a hotly contested battleground between one particular area within healthcare known as psychosomatic medicine, and another camp who doubt the entire veracity of their work. ME/CFS is the victim caught in the middle, being the illness that the 'psychosomaticians' have latched onto over the last 20-25 years as their prime example of a disease that's 'all in your head.' If they lose this fight, their entire sandcastle is in danger of collapsing. Nor did I know that there is a coterie of psychiatrists, some of whom have been shown to have links with health insurance companies, who have done everything they can to show that this disease is psychological, in order that said insurance companies can avoid paying out on claims for chronic ill health.*

*

But all this was years ahead of me. For now, having cajoled Dr K into doing a few more tests, I was dispatched to various places, and I worked my way department by department round the university hospital in Cambridge; first stop: a specialist in tropical medicine. She was excellent; the very epitome of how excellent the NHS can be when properly funded and staffed. She took detailed notes. She took lots of blood, and other bodily substances. And most of all, she took me seriously. At no point did she even hint that there might not be anything wrong with me. The difference was enormous; the small fights I had already had with Drs T and K had started to take their toll – the sense that you are having to argue with your doctor to get help, that they don't seem to believe what comes out of your mouth about the way you're feeling – these things at first seemed minor irritations. Again, only later would I come to understand how damaging they had been, and why.

*

My money was on Dengue Fever. It comes on in an instant; it can feel like a physical blow. And it gets its common name, breakbone fever, from the feeling of just that – that your bones are aching so much they seem to be about to simply crumble inside you. The intense fever, the sweats, the aching joints; I had had all these symptoms. So it had to be Dengue Fever, and that island I'd been on in Thailand; they sprayed the foliage every other day against Dengue-carrying mosquitoes. I'd been bitten by a couple

---

* Dr Michael Sharpe and Dr Simon Wessely, to name two, have both explicitly used this word; describing ME as 'the malingerers' charter' and 'the malingerers' excuse', notably when addressing employers' organisations and health insurers. More on this in the appendix.

of things there, including mosquito bites. It all made sense. Until the results came back and showed that not only did I not have Dengue Fever, but that I had *never* had Dengue Fever.

So I moved on to the next department, and the next, and the next. Blood given, MRI scans taken, tubes passed up and down my body. Still nothing, and with each nothing, a peculiar algebra started to appear in my head, as each test came back negative.

Did I want to have prostate cancer, for example?

No, of course not. But I wanted to know what was wrong.

I know from the outside how it looked – as if I wanted to find something wrong with me, and therefore as if I wanted to be ill. Reinforcing the views of those who subscribe to the malingerers' camp, no doubt. But the algebra was actually subtly different: since I *was* ill, I wanted to know what it was, and the sooner the better. I was desperate to get well, and the scary thing for me was that something felt different about this illness.

I had been ill before. Everyone has. Some of us are lucky not to have anything seriously wrong for much of our lives; others less fortunate. In my own case, I had never had the feeling that I was not going to get better. A cold, flu, food poisoning, run of the mill problems; you know all these things will pass with time. Suddenly, I didn't feel like that. Yet again possibly reinforcing the camp of those who believe it's all in the mind, very quickly this illness started to feel different to me, and one way in which it felt different was that I had rapidly lost my belief that I would recover from it.

I lay in bed and felt as if my body were collapsing, cell by cell. I could feel the disease which had entered me, taken my body hostage, and felt it pushing from the inside out; no energy, too tired sometimes to even turn over in bed; the simple act of walking, of standing for a few minutes had become something terrifying and threatening. The real, old me had been abducted, had been stolen away, and I had been placed instead inside a prison made of my own body.

Many of these feelings were hard to put into words, because I was only dimly aware of them myself. Desperation was one of the uppermost sensations I had. I had to get well, and soon. I had other trips ahead of me; the main one being to go to the States to collect the prize I'd heard about in Malaysia. But that was still four months away. Four months. Surely I'd be better by then? Time proved otherwise, and as my desperation to get well grew, I did what most people do; I had taken matters into my own hands. So I started to spend my own money, and not the taxpayers', on second opinions. I found another specialist in tropical medicine in Harley Street, for example. I found a doctor in Bath who had quit the NHS after himself getting diagnosed with CFS, and now helped people with the disease. I contacted the infamous (to the British Medical Council) Dr Sarah Myhill, who prescribes high doses of Vitamin B12 to her patients (as part of a more wide-ranging treatment protocol) and was struck off for doing so. She was only able to consult with me via email, having become swamped with patients in recent years, and so I also started to search for other less orthodox avenues of help, as I was already approaching the end of the road as far as traditional medicine was concerned.

By now, the young intern had gone back to finish her training, and my usual GP was restored to me. Dr Beattie was very sympathetic; she allowed me double the usual handful of minutes to run through everything that had happened, and at no point did she suggest I was making it up; that it was all in my head. And that very phrase had been bothering me greatly.

*

All in your head. All in the mind. What do these statements even mean? Are you literally saying that I am making it up? That I have been lying on the sofa for months on end, just because I don't feel like doing anything? Don't you know that there's almost nothing more frustrating to me than not being able to do anything?

Or maybe you don't think I'm pretending, but rather that it's psychosomatic. That my unconscious mind has, for some reason that is too obscure for anyone to see, decided to tell my body to be tired and my legs to stop functioning normally? Is that what you mean? And if that is what you mean, then does it make any difference to the way we should treat such patients? They're clearly suffering; they clearly don't want to be. Why should there be any stigma, or any less care, for the ill, if their suffering arises in their mind as opposed to their body?

Let's not even talk about an illness like epilepsy. That's literally 'all in your head' – the spasms of the brain are real, and so cause seizures, but no one would suggest telling an epileptic that it's all in their head. Or almost no one.* It's not so long ago that epilepsy too was disputed and passed off, as with CFS, as hysteria, or not much further back, as supernatural activity, as possession; later as a mental illness.

*

What bothered me deeply was that I was half-prepared to believe all this myself. I think I've always had an open mind. In fact, maybe too open. I don't think I have formed many opinions myself that I haven't had suggested to me by family or friends. Maybe that's true of most people, and anyway, I still believe that having an open mind is good. Maybe. In this case, even though I

---

* An 'award-winning science book' book of 2015 with a title very similar to this one contains supposed accounts of 'psychosomatic' epilepsy. The question of whether applying the word 'psychosomatic' to any illness is simply what doctors do when they have not yet worked out a specific biomedical model is one we'll get to later in the book.

hated the idea that my sickness might be mental in origin, and even though it seemed to me to be utter nonsense, at the same time, I was still prepared to entertain it.

Which is why when Dr Beattie told me that the officially approved strategies for working with CFS involved Cognitive Behavioural Therapy I agreed to give it a try.

I have nothing against CBT; in fact, I had had it some years before, for anxiety, with reasonably positive results. It's a rather trendy tool in the doctor's toolbox at the moment, but that doesn't mean it's of little worth. I think it's a very good tool, for the right person, with the right therapist, at the right moment. So I went along for ten weeks to the centre on the outskirts of Cambridge and worked with an intelligent and empathetic therapist of CBT, and... it did absolutely nothing for me, nor the illness. Not for the way I was feeling physically, nor for the way I felt depressed about being ill, for I have not yet mentioned that this illness had rapidly propelled me back into a place I know all too well, which is to say a place of profound and painful gloom.

I had become a misery to everyone around me, to my family, as well as to myself, and nothing I tried to do helped. Until a few weeks before, I had never been fitter in my life. That was how it seemed to me. Having not run since schooldays, I'd started walking, then running, and in a few months I had become that annoying individual pounding down country lanes on a winter's morning, looking truly smug. Timing myself over 5K, getting faster. Racing with my friend Adam when he came to stay. Pushing each other and laughing just from the fun of it. Entering a 10K race and sprinting the last K, again, just for fun. And I was that deeply annoying individual. Smug. Taking it all for granted, until BAM! Sickness arrived.

Overnight all that had gone, and if I was depressed, one thing I might defend myself over was that running was the one and only thing that I had ever found that was a deep and powerful medication for depression. As long as I ran a couple of times a week, I felt happy; I felt great, in fact. The endorphin release from exercise is now well-established and exercise is one of the few proven aids to alleviating depression. Now, not only was I ill, I had had the thing that kept my depression at bay taken away as well. And if that weren't depressing enough, my doctors were telling me the fatigue and other symptoms were a result of being depressed, and seemed unable to accept that it was the other way around; that I was depressed because I had terrible fatigue and a bunch of other unexplained symptoms. That was what was really getting to me.

That, and the fact that the other supposed cure for my tiredness was, yes, exercise.

Dr Beattie explained that the second officially approved therapy for CFS was a thing called Graded Exercise Therapy. The idea is simple. You very carefully exercise just a little, and then, gradually, you increase what you're doing, bit by bit. If that sounds to you just like a normal, sensible exercise program, you'd be right. But even at the time Dr B recommended it to me, and although I didn't yet know it, the benefit to ME/CFS patients was disputed. There is no good evidence that Graded Exercise Therapy makes any difference at all to patients with CFS. Actually, that's wrong; there is now substantial evidence showing that it can do more harm than good to people with Chronic Fatigue.[ii] That it can push people from moderate CFS into severe CFS.

*

The supposed value of both GET and CBT was based on one now-infamous study, known as the PACE trial. This trial, published in The Lancet in 2011, had apparently demonstrated that ME/CFS patients benefitted from these treatments. The trouble is that it has subsequently been shown to have been a highly flawed study, and is now generally considered to be rubbish by almost everyone apart from the people who wrote it.[iii] In related news, there is also now emerging evidence that telling people with ME/CFS that their illness is mental in origin is also doing psychological harm.[iv] Furthermore, there is a story to be told about the reason behind the drive to pass ME off as a mental health disorder; evidence of collusion between government-appointed scientists and health insurance companies on both sides of the Atlantic[v] – in writing ME off as a psychological affliction, both governments and insurers can save themselves from crippling costs. Even the very name CFS is a controversial part of this story, and I touch on it in chapter 15 and in the appendix to this book.

*

Seven years on, as I write these words, things are finally changing. After years of pressure to do so, the UK's National Institute for Health and Care Excellence (NICE) made a U-turn, announcing that neither GET or CBT should be offered as treatments for ME/CFS.[vi]

As anyone who's really listened to anyone with this illness for five minutes will tell you, this approach was just entirely wrong. There is now growing evidence that ME/CFS may be unique as being a disease that is not improved by exercise.[vii] Simply put, you cannot 'train'. It's more like you have a reserve of energy, some fuel in the tank, and when that's gone for the day, it's gone. If a car runs out of gas, you cannot get more gas into it by trying to drive it further. And thus it is with CFS. Until, with enough rest, a tiny amount slowly refills the bottom of the tank. And I am lucky, given that many people with CFS have nothing in the tank at all, bad enough to be continuously bed-ridden, to be so sensitive to light and sound they have to lie in a quiet, darkened bedroom, permanently.

*

My race was nearly run. Certainly, my days of running were over, and something deep in my body felt it was permanent.

I was reaching the end of what orthodox medicine had to say about me, and one day, with genuine kindness, Dr Beattie said that all they could say with any certainty is that I had 'Post-Infection Fatigue Syndrome', which is a slightly more specific way of saying that my Chronic Fatigue appeared after an unknown infection of some kind.

At the time of writing, in the current official view of CFS in the UK, the disease is referred to as 'biopsychosocial' – which means it's held to be a mixture of physical and psychological matters. What this means in practice, however, is rather different. The admission that there could be *any* element of psychogenesis in it is what steals the show. Give the 'malingerers' viewpoint an inch and they'll take the mile. Physical causes are ignored and the assumption made that if there's something mentally wrong, then the patient needs to get better by addressing that mental problem. Government-appointed psychologists in the UK have even stated that granting sufferers with ME/CFS disability benefits can "make patients worse",[viii] as it supposedly removes the incentive to recover – so strongly engrained is this 'malingerers' viewpoint. Imagine being someone no longer able to work, relying on those benefits, and then being told they're going to take the benefits away because they're making you not get better. It's hard to think of many things more insulting, or more cruel.

Meanwhile, as I write, the view of ME/CFS in the United States has recently changed. In America, the illness is now officially and explicitly recognised as a biophysical disease, according to the latest word from the National Institute of Health. This disparity between the UK and the US is striking, and the cause of growing contention; what is at stake, as we'll see later, is not just the battleground of what ME/CFS is or isn't; it's much, much more than that: it's a war that threatens to undermine the entire validity of the relatively small and mysterious field of healthcare known as psychosomatic medicine.

That war is something I had glimpsed in that moment when my doctor told me my illness was all in my head. I didn't yet know consciously, I couldn't have expressed then what is so clear to me now, the reason for the shock when she uttered those words; the reason the ground shifted slightly under my feet. Now I can, and it's this: in modern Western secular society, there is probably no one that the average person holds in more respect, esteem and reverence than one's doctor. In the absence of priests, with our modern disdain for politicians and other persons in positions of power, the doctor is our last remaining mystic. You are sick; you turn to them for help. You may be worried, even scared, and you go to them assuming, *expecting* that they will help you, or at the very least will do their best to do so. If what you get instead is rejection, dismissal of your fears, and an intimation or even the explicit statement that you're imagining the whole thing, the repercussions are strong; they are deeply damaging.

*

Back in 2014, in those first bewildering months, my tiredness, Dr B told me, was a result of 'deconditioning'. That is to say, yes, I had been ill, with something unknown, but now I was just tired because I had been lying around for several weeks. I tried to point out that I had been tired from the very start, that I had been running happily just the week before, that the specific nature of the tiredness now was exactly the same as when it had arrived overnight, that even gentle attempts to walk made me worse, not better. I could not have 'deconditioned' overnight. I didn't get anywhere with any of this.

She said she thought I'd probably pull through in the end, since she knew I was not the type to 'settle into it'. At least she didn't say malingerer. And she wished me well.

Seven years on, I have finally formed my own opinion about something. While doctors have told me I have the thing known as Chronic Fatigue Syndrome, I find this classification as useless as it is pedantically accurate. It is merely your doctor telling you what you told her in the first place; you're tired all the time with a bunch of related other odd symptoms. Therefore, I have come to refer to myself as suffering from 'Undiagnosis'; a term as accurate as it is also pedantically useless, but one that I now prefer, for its honesty. Even if people look at me strangely when I use it.

But this is a major part of being ill with a chronic, undiagnosed illness. You become your own doctor. You have to. Once orthodox medicine is done with you, you have two choices: lie at home and try to forget about it, get on with life in whatever limited way you can, or do what you can on your own terms to find an answer. There has to be *something* wrong with me, whether it's mental or physical. And, therefore, I am determined to find what that something is. That's how the second school of thought goes, and it's in that school that I quickly enrolled myself, albeit involuntarily.

As I mentioned above, becoming your own doctor is something that appears to severely irritate actual doctors. We went to medical school for years to learn all we know, they say. You will do yourself more harm than good by reading things on the internet with no medical training. We have the knowledge; you don't.

Unfortunately, it's not as simple as that. For example, once you come across genuine, peer-reviewed academic studies that rubbish the PACE trial, over and over again, it's pretty hard to keep having confidence in the doctor that is recommending CBT or GET to you. You don't just lose confidence in the individual doctor either; you begin to lose faith in the entire system they represent.

On top of which, you start to uncover articles that seem to suggest new routes for enquiry; things that you know will take years to become verified science, years further to develop treatment protocols, years after that to 'reach market'. Try to talk about one of those things to your common or garden GP, and you will more often than not be met with a lack of interest, or perhaps just, very simply, a lack of knowledge. Of course, not every doctor can keep up with the cutting edge of medical research, but once again, these things drive a wedge between you and your doctor.

All this was something else I would be forced to consider as the years rolled by, another little consequence of being told it's 'all in your head.'

Meanwhile, there was another group of people that was giving me concern. My friends.

---

i Virginia Woolf, *On Being Ill*, The New Criterion, London, 1926
ii For Example:
https://www.researchgate.net/publication/216572185_Reporting_of_ Harms_Associated_with_Graded_Exercise_Therapy_and_Cognitive_ Behavioural_Therapy_in_Myalgic_EncephalomyelitisChronic_Fatigue _Syndrome
iii For example: https://www.statnews.com/2016/09/21/chronic-fatigue-syndrome-pace-trial/
iv For example:
https://www.ncbi.nlm.nih.gov/pmc/articles/PMC6567989/
v http://www.margaretwilliams.me/2003/notes-on-insurance-issue-in-me.pdf
vi https://www.bmj.com/content/371/bmj.m4356
vii Hodges LD, Nielsen T, Baken D. Physiological measures in participants with chronic fatigue syndrome, multiple sclerosis and healthy controls following repeated exercise: a pilot study. Clin Physiol Funct Imaging. 2018 Jul;38(4):639-644. doi: 10.1111/cpf.12460. Epub 2017 Aug 7. PMID: 28782878.
viii Psychiatrist Simon Wessely, one of the originators of the biopsychosocial model of ME, in a 1993 meeting with Nicholas Scott, MP, Minister for the Disabled. For the full horror of this go here: https://forums.phoenixrising.me/threads/simon-wessely-and-his-statement-benefits-can-often-make-these-patients-worse-1993.31475/

3 – But You Don't Look Ill

'To be ill is an unforgiveable sin.' So runs a traditional German maxim. I'd never heard it at the time I got sick, but its underlying meaning was going to be presented to me soon, and frequently. No one likes it when you're ill.

Doctors were one thing. Friends and family another. Up until this point, I had more or less every confidence in the medical profession. I'd naively assumed that your doctors would go on trying to fix you until you were better, or dead. I had not, for one second, imagined that they'd suggest you were faking it. Or maybe even that your unconscious is faking it, to be charitable. So it had come as a shock to be dealing with disbelief and doubt from the very people you had turned to for help. But there was another surprise in store; I wasn't ready for the reaction from friends.

*

'But you don't look ill.'

That was what I started to hear, in some variety or other, over and over again. Friends who had heard I was ill came to see us, there were people I saw through work, more distant parts of my family.

'But you don't look ill.'

Oh good, then I must be fine.

I don't want to sound mean or ungrateful, though I'm sure I might. I suppose that people were just saying what was in their head, and most likely meant it as an expression of relief. They'd heard I was sick, something I'd picked up in Asia, the doctors didn't know what to do. They may have thought I was at death's door, and would look like it. Seeing me sitting on a sofa, at home, with a nice suntan from two weeks in the sun, I didn't look ill. At all. I still, often, have people tell me how well I look, over a Zoom call. I don't know how to reply, given that I feel awful. And then, sometimes, someone will say, *you look really tired*, and I think to myself, do you believe me now? Such is the paranoia of not being believed that has taken root in me.

Seeing me at a meeting in a publisher's office for an hour, no one would know how hard it had been waiting for two or three minutes to be invited to sit down; how tiring the journey to London had been; how I was having to spend a fortune to get taxis everywhere so I could be dropped at the door rather than walk from the underground; how long I'd spend in bed later that day, and the next, maybe more, having pushed myself too far.

The idea that to be ill is a sin is one with a long history, and, being a sin, is a concept of religious origin. Around the time I was first ill, my daughter was writing an essay at school about the medieval notion of suffering; that suffering brings us closer to God. This view is clearly expressed in the work from which the epigraph to this book comes.

In 1624, metaphysical poet and cleric John Donne published his *Devotions Upon Emergent Occasions, and severall steps in my Sicknes*, which opens:

Variable, and therefore miserable condition of man! this minute I was well, and am ill, this minute. I am surprised with a sudden change, and alteration to worse, and can impute it to no cause, nor call it by any name.

It was written the previous December as Donne succumbed to, nearly died of, and recovered from, some unknown illness, perhaps typhus or a fever of some other kind. It's a quotable text; this is the origin of both 'no man is an island' and 'for whom the bell tolls'. The work is divided into 23 sections, representing the 23 days of his illness. Each is subdivided into a 'meditation', an 'expostulation' and a prayer, as Donne focusses on thoughts around and stages of the illness each day, draws a religious interpretation of these ideas, and then concludes with a prayer –

the whole thing designed to reinforce the view that illness is a visitation of God, reflecting the sin of the individual concerned, and that through this suffering we move closer to God.

O miserable condition of man! which was not imprinted by God, who, as he is immortal himself, had put a coal, a beam of immortality into us, which we might have blown into a flame, but blew it out by our first sin…

So exclaims Donne, in the first of these feverish 23 meditations, continuing;

O multiplied misery! we die, and cannot enjoy death, because we die in this torment of sickness; … we joined an artificial sickness of our own melancholy, to our natural, our unnatural fever. O perplexed discomposition, O riddling distemper, O miserable condition of man!

Written, according to Donne himself, during the course of the illness, with "near super-human speed and concentration", it does read like some strange fever dream, something that modern voices have not always been very generous about. A critic of 1924, exactly 300 years after first publication, said of *Devotions* that "It is too introspective, too metaphysical, too much overloaded with learning of different kinds",[i] (remarks that could easily be directed at the book you hold in your hands currently). And seven years later, another modern voice held that it was the product of an "anxious and restless mind".[ii] Ditto. No doubt John Donne was anxious as he wrote in his state of illness, lasting 23 days. Heaven help, therefore, the writer who writes after seven years of illness, or more…

Why are we so uncomfortable around the subject of illness? A matter to return to a little later. Meanwhile, I was still taking the first of *severall steps* on the journey of my own *sicknes*.

*

We were literally talking about steps.

'Pacing,' that was the only other advice the good Dr Beattie had given me. 'You have to learn to pace yourself. You know, people who get ME are generally of the same personality type. Type 'A's. Always rushing, always pushing. Burning the candle at both ends. Anxious. High achievers. Does any of this sound like you?'

She already knew me well enough to know that it did. Her advice was that since I had but a little energy, I had to learn to spend it more wisely. To be aware of my expenditure of the stuff down to how many steps I took each day. But, even though I was sick, I found I still could not say 'no' to things. I still tried to push on, to go to meetings, to give talks, even though I would pay for it later.

*

'But you don't look ill.'

After 'all in your head', these five words set me off on a detour in my journey, wondering about what exactly we mean by health, and by illness. Where the borderline is. And how some illnesses are more 'acceptable', in a variety of ways, than others. Imagine if, on top of having cancer, or Parkinson's, that people told you that you were faking it, or imagining it. That you weren't 'really' ill. This, for many people, is the lived experience of ME/CFS. It now struck me that, as apparently the Germans knew all along, really, to be ill at all is rather selfish. I say apparently because, though I was told that maxim by an apparently fluent German speaker, it turns out not to be true. I mean, it isn't an old German expression, or if it is, it's so obscure that none of the ten or so German native speakers I have asked since have ever heard of it.

*

The trouble was, the damage had been done; the thought was in my head. I realised it expressed something I had been feeling anyway; feeling guilty for being ill, as if it was my fault. Perhaps it *was* my fault. Perhaps I should have taken better care of myself; perhaps when I thought I was healthy, I was something slightly different; I was *fit*. I could run, I could push myself, and so on, but thinking back, I see there were warnings signs. A couple of trips to the doctor because I was breathless from time to time, for no apparent reason; another for constant heart palpitations. Nothing was found to be amiss; I was sent away and the symptoms ebbed eventually in each case. I could now see that these were obvious signs of stress; what amazes me is that no doctor pointed this out to me at the time. Still, one's health is one's own affair. And if you get ill, that must be your affair too.

When I was breathless, when I had palpitations, I kept on working, and though I was not writing, I kept on working now too, as best I could, doing public appearances. This ability to keep on working or socializing at all must have again reinforced the 'all in your head' camp.

*

And friends... illness is much like death; many people simply do not want to hear about it. End of story, conversation closed. I was again at first surprised by the people who simply could not, *would* not hear me even *mention* that I was sick. The mute embarrassment they showed was a pretty clear signal, however, and I learned to try keep my importunate illness to myself. The link between illness and death is obvious, but both for me have never been things not to talk about.

Much of my writing had dealt with death, in fictional form – it had always seemed to me that there is no better or safer way to try to come to terms with our own mortality than through fiction. I still believe that. I suspect that a lot of my early success in writing books predominantly read by younger people was that teenagers are starved of conversations in real life about difficult matters like death, and some of my books were among those that dealt with death openly and honestly. The teenage experience is not a particularly easy one, and it's also one, I believe, with which the majority of the adult world does not offer much help. There are a number of reasons for this: for one thing, adults are busy doing all that mystifying and terrifying 'adult' stuff, the stuff we dreaded ever having to cope with ourselves when we were teenagers: jobs, taxes, in-laws, whatever it may be. And secondly, and maybe more importantly, most people never come to terms with the outrageously alarming concepts that generally are first encountered in the teenage years: things like sex and relationships, and above all, a true conception of death. That clichéd nihilistic cry of the teenager, 'what is the meaning of life?' with the closely-following suspicion that there just isn't one, is something that I suspect the majority of adults in the modern world never made any kind of peace with. No conclusion was made, no resolution found. We hurry as soon as we can out of the mess of being a teenager, and hide ourselves from it with exactly that adult stuff we once feared: the jobs, the taxes, the obligations to family and friends. Until a crisis hits. Until it happens to you.

Whatever the cause, we do not help teenagers with this stuff – sex and death – sufficiently. If you cast your mind back to those years (and I have more than once had middle-aged people end up in tears in writing workshops when I suggest they do, sometimes angry tears) you may yourself remember asking a parent or teacher about something to do with death, or the fear of it. If you got anything better than an evasion, a dismissive wave of the hand, a glossing of the obvious horror, then you are lucky. At best, we tend to patronize our teenagers; underestimating constantly what they are capable of dealing with, while denying them what they need and want to wrestle with, because of the unresolved fear it brings back in us.

That the teenage mind, therefore, appreciates anyone who is not patronizing about matters like death and illness should not be wondered at, and for those young adults that read, there is a way out: fiction. By way of evidence to show this is not just my fantasy, I get letters from younger readers stating this fact explicitly.

Adults, however, are a funny bunch. And when I say funny, I mean odd. I often joke with my daughter that the one true thing I taught her is that 'people are weird', and I guess it worked since she went off to university to study Psychology. Though we joke about it, we both agree that the *truly* weird thing is that everyone thinks they're normal. From inside each of us, we act rationally, basing our decisions and thoughts and actions on every action and thought and decision we have had before, on everything that has happened to us. The older we get, therefore, the further down a very lengthy, convoluted and *individual* road we all find ourselves. And we may, more or less, consciously know that we behave a certain way in a certain situation because of what happened to us, but either way, we think we are behaving rationally. It only looks weird from the outside. So when you realise that you have a friend who never apologises no matter what the circumstances, or when you discover a work colleague is always late deliberately, when you see some people utterly refuse to wear a mask during a pandemic because it will 'infringe their liberty' despite the risk they run of infringing the liberty of everyone they encounter by infecting them, there is no doubt a lifelong series of reasons why they behave the way they do, and they feel perfectly right behaving that way.

Since teenagers have been around for a shorter length of time, and since our starting places are finite, I find it is generally easier to understand young people's fears and foibles than those of us who have been on the planet for a longer period of time (as a French doctor kindly said about my age one day.)

All this is a long-winded way of saying that it should come as no great surprise that adults often do not want to be confronted by death, nor by illness, especially in the modern, secular, western world, where we have done our level best to remove all sight and sound of both these spectres from everyday life. Our ill now die in hospitals and hospices; our old live out the end of their lives in retirement homes, not in the family seat. We have all the modern accoutrements of mortuaries and funeral homes to deal with the icky stuff, and the vast world that is a Death is passed off in fifteen minutes on a rainy afternoon around a hole in the ground and an hour or two in the pub. (I say that this is how it's passed off; the truth is that this is probably how it *isn't* passed off; how we become stuck with unresolved grief.) The pandemic has brought so much of this closer to the surface of everyday life. Now that the whole world is watching death, these matters can be ignored no longer. We all know of people who have died of Covid-19. It has become harder to push the thought of death away successfully, a fact underlined by the extreme ways some reacted to the pandemic during its first year. Probably as you have, I have heard many stories of friends and family falling out; some fearful, others brazen, divided by their varying views on isolation, masks, confinement and so on.

Yet, before the pandemic put death and sickness at the forefront of everyone's minds, it came as a surprise to me that some people I thought to be good friends slowly and quietly dropped out of my life. I suppose it is just too much for some to be reminded of our frailty as humans, and I can't judge them for that. We all have our own weirdnesses to bear, while suffering from them because we still think we're being rational. I should also immediately say that others were wonderful, and listened to me and kept in touch more than before, and did the small things friends do that in big ways show you that they are feeling for you. Yet, overall, I was struck by the impression of people letting me go, of people silently requesting my own silence. As a culture, we do not want to know about illness. We do not want to know about illness unless it comes in a very specific form: usually, *the narrative of recovery*. More of that later.

*

Here too, I have to confess my own sins. As much as some people slid out of my life, I let others slide. In fact, I probably encouraged some to disappear. I saw myself doing it, very early on, and was at a loss to explain it to myself, if I even tried to, which wasn't often. If I did, I just told myself, it's no wonder I can't cope with lots of people right now. I'm tired.

*

I'm tired. I'm tired, I'm tired, I'm tired.

All the time, all day, every day. I was sick of hearing myself say it, no wonder if other people were too. And yet I could not stop myself. I'm tired, I'm tired, I'm tired. There was nothing else to say, for there was nothing else in me.

Only after several years did I realise why I was saying it all the time – because, each utterance of the word didn't even come close to how I was feeling. Everyone knows the word. Tired. It doesn't come close to expressing the nature of the exhaustion that is the primary symptom of ME/CFS. Just as Virginia Woolf said all those years ago, we do not have the subtlety of vocabulary when we speak about illness. For the tiredness that comes with ME/CFS is so much more than the word as we usually use it. I used to quite like being tired – that pleasant sense of having had a busy day or a late night or a good run; flopping onto the sofa or into bed, safe in the knowledge that when you rise, you will rise with ease, and your body will be restored to its happy self, and you will be ready for what comes next. Not so with this disease. The tiredness comes from nowhere, from doing nothing, and it is never relieved with rest. In fact, one of the items in the ME/CFS (lack of-) diagnosis checklist is; a fatigue that is unalleviated by rest or sleep. This is why some people prefer to call it malaise, especially the terrible extra crash, and mounting of symptoms that comes with any kind of exertion, known to 'us in the trade' as PEM - Post Exertional Malaise. This is not a pleasant kind of tiredness. This is not have-a-nap-and-you'll-be-right-as rain-afterwards tiredness. This is awful. It is a nightmare of collapse in your body's functioning, in which it feels as if every cell in you is screaming for mercy, tortured and imprisoned. And years of experiencing it almost continually have shown me the impossibility of really conveying the nature of it to someone who thinks that people with ME/CFS are just feeling a bit under the weather, or, whisper it behind their backs, lazy.

*

But all this didn't explain why I was letting people drop out of my life, and I have to be honest, in some cases cutting them out. People I loved, and who had loved me. I started to cut them out, and I had no idea why. If I did think about it, I would try to analyse myself; you're motivated by something, what is it? What did that person do or say? Have they offended you? What are you getting by not seeing them, or writing to them?

I came up with few, and always unconvincing arguments. That friend who'd told me I ought to be excited to go on a trip to Asia, when I'd said I was in truth not looking forward to it. Was that why I'd cut him out; that I unconsciously blamed him for going, and thus getting ill? Maybe. It seemed weak to me, and he was a good friend.

Was it just a matter of energy again? Did I just want to save it for the people and things that really mattered to me? Maybe. It didn't feel like the whole truth.

For whatever reason, the number of people in my life began to reduce. Maybe it was just necessary in some way, and here I'm reminded of the friend and neighbour who'd told me six months or so into my illness that it could be that my illness was 'the universe sending me what I needed'.

I wasn't aware I *needed* to be ill, and you can easily imagine what I felt about this statement, but to my credit I at least managed not to reply anything beyond a mumbled, 'yes, maybe.'

Maybe, maybe, maybe. Another mantra. Maybe it's this, maybe it's that. Maybe I'm ill in my head, maybe in my body. Maybe I'll get better, maybe I won't.

*

Time rolled on. Four or five months in, the trip to Las Vegas to collect the award I'd won came around, and I wasn't better as I'd assumed I would be. People asked me if I was nervous about the speech, and in a way I was; not because of making the speech itself, but of having to stand for the fifteen minutes or so it would take. On the day, I forgot something in my room and had to go back, just before the ceremony began. No big deal if you can walk easily; for me, in the size of a vast American conference hotel, it was like walking to the moon and back. But the speech went okay, and there was just one moment when the brain fog that so often accompanies CFS kicked in and, halfway through what I was saying, I totally lost track. I stood silent, blinking at the crowd and my heart began to sink. Now I would make an ass of myself in front of people whose opinion mattered to me. Now I would die of embarrassment. But I was lucky; to the audience it sounded as if I had paused for dramatic effect, to emphasise the last thing I'd said, as if I meant it to be taken as some very important point. I hadn't at all, but whatever it was, after a second or two of silence they audience started applauding, during which time I hauled up something else to say. It was fine. My legs were screaming at me. I slept.

And so the months rolled on again until I had been ill for a year, and nothing had changed, and I knew that another big thing had arrived in my life: not knowing.

[i] Simpson, Evelyn, *A Study of the Prose Works of John Donne*. Clarendon Press, 1924

[ii] White, Helen C, *English Devotional Literature 1600–1640. University of Wisconsin. Studies in language and literature. Madison, 1931*

4 – Undiagnosis

'Say: "my name is Mary",' said Dr G.

'My name is Mary,' I said, and as I did so, he easily pushed my outstretched arm down, which I was supposed to be trying to resist.

'There!' he said. 'You see? That's how it works. The brain knows when you're lying.'

'Oh,' I said. 'Yes. Of course.'

Maybe I had better back up a bit.

*

The full horror of not knowing had started to sink in.

I was desperate to find out what was wrong with me, and should proof of this be needed, a look back through my diary in that first year yields a bewildering array of appointments. Some of them are of the more, and some of the very much *less* orthodox kind. As for the latter, I have always been somewhat caught somewhere on the spectrum between gullible and cynical, though if pushed I would probably fall into the cynics' camp. There are those people who believe in all the weird, flaky, new-age 'woo' stuff going, and those who believe in none of it. I was always unhappy with either extreme viewpoint – it seems the height of arrogance to think that we know all there is to know, and the very essence of science, as any truly wise scientist will tell you, is about moving from not knowing to knowing. Eventually. Maybe. Anyone who confidently dismisses homeopathy, and may be right to do so, is also no doubt the person who confidently would have dismissed allergy testing previously, and would have been wrong to do so. But, similarly, the other extreme point of view, of unquestioning faith in the most unlikely therapies, based on theories that are questionable at best and laughable and fraudulent at worst, also seems dangerous. I get sad thinking about this kind of belief, because I suspect what underlies people's gullibility in such things is two powerful forces: fear and desperation.

Fear and desperation. I was starting to experience my fair share of both, and I could see that this was pushing me into trying things I would not normally have given the time of day. Alongside, I continued with more traditional medical routes, things which, though they were outside of what the health service had decided could be done, were still based on 'accepted' science. More or less.

*

For the record, then, here's a list of who I consulted in the first *five* years:

General Practitioners – 7
Specialists in tropical medicine and infectious diseases – 2
Rheumatologist – 1
'Orthodox' medical specialists in Chronic Fatigue Syndrome – 3
Practitioners of various 'alternative' therapies for CFS – 4
Allergist – 1
Homeopaths – 2
Acupuncturists – 2
Osteopaths – 2
Chiropractor – 1
Cranial-Sacral Therapist -1
Internists – 2
Haematologists – 3
Massage Therapists – 3
Nutritionists – 3
Herbalist – 1
Cognitive Behavioural Therapist – 1
Interpersonal Therapist –1
Neurologist – 1

Balneotherapist – 1
Myofascial Release Therapist – 1
Hypnotists – 2
Remote Healers – 1
Jungian Psychologists – 2
Urologists – 2
Dialectical Behaviour Therapist – 1
EMDR Therapist – 1
Reflexologist – 1
Reiki Master – 1

That's a list of over 50 people I consulted in the first five years in an effort to recover. I have probably missed one or two. There have been more since. There were also many blood tests I paid for directly with labs around the world, the quality of which I had no way of even estimating, but which I was driven to from fear and desperation; those scheming co-conspirators. I dare not add up exactly how much money I have spent in the process. It is in the tens of thousands of pounds. Many, many people do not have the money at all to pursue lines of enquiry like these therapies, none of which made the slightest bit of difference to how I actually felt, with one or two exceptions, which we'll come to much later. Similarly, almost none of it even helped me understand what was going on, take even one step towards understanding what was actually wrong with me, to move out of the place of not knowing. Almost none of it, I say, and though there are a couple of exceptions, they come with warnings attached.

I said earlier that this is not a self-help book. It is a book with many more questions than answers, and it is not a 'how I beat' ME/CFS handbook. There are some things I have learned about the illness, which I didn't know at the outset, but I will disappoint you now and let you know that this book does not conclude with me getting physically better. If we have to hear an illness narrative at all, those are generally the kind of narratives we want to hear; the ones where people get better. The narrative of recovery; the redoubtable human spirit overcoming the odds, no matter how great. If you've come here looking for that kind of happy ending, I'm sorry. If you do find a book like that about ME/CFS, which actually works, please let me know. And despite what I said right at the start, there is an ending to this book, one that emerged as I wrote it and rewrote it, but it's not one I ever expected. That these two statements – *this book has no ending*, but also, *this book has an ending* – are not contradictory, is something I will try to explain when we get there.

*

I should also reassure any remaining readers who have not now closed the book and hurled it across the room that I am not going to take you through all fifty-something of these consultations. I'll spare you that, as I wish I could have spared myself. So I'll pass rapidly over the homeopath who, after I'd left a message saying I might not come back for more sessions, phoned me up and told me I 'very likely' had radiation sickness from flying long-haul over Asia. I'll skip around the Jungian analyst who, after a single, embarrassingly bad session, which left me feeling I could have done a better job myself, also phoned me back saying I had to return at least once so she could 'close the hole she'd left in my psyche'. I shall not mention the remote healer who asked me to send photographs of myself naked ('and wearing no metal') from front and back so she could study my aural energy. In each case, I am sure they genuinely meant well, and were trying to help; they just didn't. There were many more ineffective treatments and consultations too, which I will mostly ignore, though I am going to drop in on one or two of the more illuminating sessions, and that brings me back to where I was just asserting that my name is Mary.

*

In case there's any doubt, I knew my name was not Mary. I might have been living in a state of not knowing, but I still knew what I was called. I'd gone to see Dr G in Bath, at the advice of some new acquaintances; the husband said he'd had a period of a couple of years when he had no energy, was tired all the time, and that Dr G had helped. Sort of. From the way he described it, it didn't sound exactly like me, but it was worth a shot. By this point, given that I'd conceded to my mother's exhortations and consulted a reiki master, you can see that anything felt like it was worth a shot. (The reiki was very calming. I lay on a couch in a darkened room and the reiki master laid her hands on me; she then told me to make sure I spent a good portion of each day outside barefoot and that she would send the energy required to make me better. I need not say this didn't work or I probably wouldn't be writing this. And if Reiki has worked for someone else, I am truly happy to hear it. I do not scorn Reiki as I once did. For one thing, illness teaches you humility, eventually. For another thing, I have changed the way I think about the mind and body.)

*

So to Bath. I drove to see Dr G. He welcomed me at the door of his home from where he was practising, a man more or less of my generation, which is to say middle-aged. He wore a tracksuit, like he'd just been jogging or sparring or generally doing something energetic.

'Do I have the right time?' I ventured.

'Sure,' he said, 'come on in,' and he settled me into his consulting room.

The meeting started off well. He explained how he had been a GP working within the orthodox healthcare system, but had grown frustrated about what he was and wasn't allowed to do, and so had set up privately to practise a more integrated form of medicine. He explained how he himself had had Chronic Fatigue Syndrome, for many months, and how he had 'experimented' on himself, in an effort to work out what was wrong. By this, he meant he had seen what made his symptoms worse, what if anything made them better, and so on, and in the end he had cured himself.

'So, you're saying I can get better?' I asked.

'Yes,' he said, 'of course. But it depends what you mean by better.'

I started to sense a warning bell in my head.

'By better, I mean, well... Will I be able to run again?'

'Run, yes. Thrash yourself to death in training, no. I've been able to start jogging again. Nice and gently. That business of pushing yourself, that's one of the things that made you ill. You won't be able to go back to that. You don't want to.'

Ok. That made sense. The Type-A thing again. Pushing, pushing until you break yourself.

I was still unsure about what he had in mind, and what his cure would be, but then from out of nowhere, he pulled out a couple of things that knocked me down.

*

Undiagnosis is different for everyone. Even within the part of Undiagnosis we call ME or Chronic Fatigue Syndrome, people experience a wide-ranging gamut of different though often overlapping symptoms. 'Diagnosis' for CFS, such as it is, is a diagnosis *by exclusion* of other possible causes on the part of your doctor, and then a question of ticking off a number of symptoms on the official list. 'Have you been ill for more than six months and can you check four or more of the list below...?' That kind of thing. One of the things that probably drives healthcare professionals mad about people with CFS is that the symptoms vary from person to person; yes, everyone is tired, but even the nature of that can vary, and accompanying symptoms can be a different set from patient to patient. Again, this is a lesson that has been brought home to more of us since the pandemic of 2020. The fact that symptoms of the virus can vary so widely, that people can have it and be completely asymptomatic, that the tests used early on were so very inaccurate… all these things should have reinforced to the general public that being a doctor must, to be honest, be a total nightmare at times.

In the many consultations with GPs I'd had by this point, I had tried to offer them all the clues I could about my symptoms. I had assumed they would want to know, like a private detective would want as many clues as possible to solve a case. I was wrong. If I tried to add in that I still had earache, or that I kept on feeling like was getting a cold, it never came to anything; they would literally ignore me, as if I hadn't spoken. I suppose I was making things harder from their point of view.

But now, Dr G, and before I had even really told him much about my illness, or how it had come on, said this:

'I imagine you often feel like you're coming down with a cold, but it never comes to anything?'

'Yes, yes, that's right,' I said, amazed. Relieved, in fact, that someone not only had finally taken note of it, but that he had brought it up in the first place. I was already suspicious of quackery, and this reassured me this wasn't something I'd mentioned that he'd just repeated back to me, like a fake stage medium doing cold reading.

'How did you know?' I added.

And he explained that it was all part of my immune system not functioning properly. How my killer cells were on high alert and were out on the prowl, as if there was an intruder in my body, like a cold virus, even though there wasn't one.

'It's the over-activity of immune cells in your body that are giving you that feeling.'

And if I needed any more convincing that he might actually know what he was talking about, and again before I'd discussed it, he told my how my legs probably felt like jelly most of the time, and he gave me the explanation for that too.

This was great. Not the feeling of weak legs. But of finally meeting someone who knew what I was going through, and more importantly, why.

'Oh,' I said, 'I see. Right. Well, this is all very encouraging. So what do I do about it?'

'Well, in my case, I worked out a formulation of high doses of certain vitamins and minerals.'

'Okay,' I said.

I'd been down this route already, with the protocol of the infamous Dr Sarah Myhill, still the best-known doctor in the UK taking people with CFS seriously, and getting results it seems. I say 'infamous' because she was struck off the NHS medical register for prescribing high doses of Vitamin B12 to her patients. (Despite the fact that, as she says herself, the only way you could kill yourself taking too much B12 is if you fell in a vat of the stuff and drowned.) I didn't actually get to see Dr Myhill in person; she was so swamped with desperate requests for help that she only offers new patients consultations by email and blood test, and that after a wait of many weeks. But I had hope for Dr G's similar methods, and there was no harm in having two experts in CFS giving me more or less the same treatment. Lots of vitamins and minerals, rest, a relaxed attitude, and, most importantly, enough time for it all to work.

'The only question we have to consider first,' Dr G went on, 'is whether you still have an infection of some kind.'

'Ah' I said. 'Yes. I see. And how can we –'

'I'm also a trained kinesiologist. I assume you know what kinesiology is?'

I thought maybe it was something like osteopathy, but I wasn't sure, so I shook my head and he told me a little about it.

'So, would you like to go ahead?'

Well, I thought, I tried reiki. And he'd been absolutely spot on about the feeling-like-you're-getting-a-cold-even-though-you-aren't thing. And I'd come all this way. So...

'Sure,' I said.

*

Dr G ran through the basics.

I sat on the edge of his treatment table, and he told me to hold my right arm out to the side, bent back at the elbow, so I was touching my shoulder with my hand.

'Now,' he said, 'I'm going to push down, and I want you to resist it.'

He did, and I did, and he couldn't push my arm down. After a second or two, he stopped trying.

'Now, say: "My name is Mary."'

'Er... my name is Ma –'

He pushed my arm down in an instant, and with ease.

'There! You can't lie to your brain. It's so busy processing the untruth, that you can't resist my pushing at the same time.'

'Oh. Yes.'

'So what we do next is we put a series of these phials in your left hand, and I try to push down your right arm again.'

'Ah. Right. Got it.'

He'd produced a set of elaborate wooden cases, with small compartments inside, each containing a small glass phial, inside of which were various mysterious substances. Green things. Brown things. Grey lumps. Some of them seemed to contain nothing at all.

'We'll test for the right things: viruses, bacteria. Candida, that's a yeast overgrowth, you know.'

'Yes, right.'

'And if I can push your arm down while you're holding a particular phial, that means your brain knows that it's a lie, by which I mean, it knows that it's not true that you have what's in the phial. Clear?'

'Um–'

'Good.'

So off we went. We rattled through the big ones; viruses, bacteria. All negative, thank heaven. The magic phials and my magic-lie-detecting brain did their work; that and Dr G pushing my arm down each time. Candida, negative. Heavy metal poisoning. Negative. Everything, negative, negative, negative.

'Great,' Dr G declared. 'You're in the clear. So we can start you on the vitamins. I'll provide you with a list of the best suppliers. You have to use decent stuff. That's very important.'

And five minutes later, I was out in my car and driving home, trying to work out what had happened.

I later learned that the business with the phials was something called Applied Kinesiology – part of a toolkit that Dr G was working with; the stuff the NHS wouldn't have let him do, presumably. To me, that second part of the consultation had been complete whackery, and yet, he'd made total sense during the first part. He was the very first doctor I had seen who'd actually been able to not only describe what was happening to me almost better than I could, but *why*. And that really meant something to me. But did the second part ruin the first? Or did that not matter?

Can you declare that all the ravings of a madman are just that, even if he sometimes speaks the truth? Or, to put it another way, if truth comes out of the mouth of a madman, does that stop it from being true? To be clear, I am speaking metaphorically, and Dr G was clearly not crazy. He was just working with a tool I found myself unable to believe in, and that left me unsure as to whether I could trust the rest of his appraisal of me, which I found sound. Since this was the first real ray of hope I'd seen, I felt it would hurt to have to let it go. So I didn't. I bought the vitamins and minerals he'd suggested at around £30 for a month's supply of each one, and off I went, popping pills over breakfast every morning. Mountains of pills.

But with every pill I took, I wondered whether I was helping myself, or just wasting my money, and the months went by and nothing happened, nothing at all. I didn't even get worse.

*

Once again, it was clear that when you get sick with an undiagnosed illness, you have to become your own doctor. When the 'real' doctors give up on you, you have to do your own research. You go and see less 'orthodox' doctors, but even then, you have to pick and choose what you believe to be true. How you do that is... what? Random? A matter of faith, or instinct? I am not a doctor; I have no more than a rudimentary understanding of science from four A-Levels at school, and that was a long time ago. But, somehow, you start to pick through the overwhelming quantity of information in front of you, and try to make sense of it. That was what I had done, with Dr G and his account of my illness. I'd accepted the vitamins, but rejected the little glass phials as easily as I had rejected the idea that my name was Mary.

Again, this process of self-diagnosis is something millions more of us have now experienced, in the face of overwhelmed medical services. The countless stories of particularly young people being turned away from hospitals, even though they were symptomatic; the utterly inadequate levels of testing in most countries; especially shameful in some of the richest countries on Earth – the United States, the United Kingdom – the living with daily fear – is this just a normal sort of cough, or am I going to die? – all these things are now familiar to many. Yet there is a difference. Outside of a few extreme people like a neighbour of mine who believed it was a conspiracy to allow the unimpeded building of 5G masts, no one doubts that Covid-19 exists. Few people genuinely think it's not real, though they do exist. Millions of dollars have and are being spent urgently improving tests, developing vaccines, funding the construction of respirators, building hospitals, and so on. For those with ME/CFS, and related conditions, there is *almost* total silence on the part of the medical world. Outside of a few shining lights of research, who are making encouraging progress, living with ME/CFS is more or less like living in the middle ages, as far as medical expertise goes.

So you have to become your own doctor, and not only are you not a very good doctor, it's also a very lonely road to follow. Such is the nature of Undiagnosis.

5 – Frog's Legs at the Centre of the World

'But there's no such illness,' Dr Mugnier said.

Eighteen months or so into my illness, and I'd moved to France.

Life in Cambridge was nice, and quiet. But not quite quiet enough. That village of 200 hundred people seemed too much for me. I wondered if living an unobtrusive life on a mountainside might be the magic bullet to make me better. Stop making author appearances, breathe pure mountain air, de-stress. It was worth a try, and I figured, even if it didn't work and I was still ill, at least I could be ill where the views were better and the wine was cheaper.

I'd been working our way through various administrative things, and getting registered with the local medical centre was the next thing to do. I sat in front of Dr Mugnier for a little welcome chat. I was there for over 45 minutes. It was hard to conceive of, given how little time you get in front of a GP in the UK or the United States. He wanted to talk about this and that; he asked me where I'd been living before.

'Cambridge,' I told him. 'Well, in a small village outside Cambridge.'

'Cambridge, a pretty town,' he said, laughing, 'but now you're in the centre of the world.'

It was an interesting way of putting it. Some people I had told about the move wondered why I wanted to go and live in the middle of nowhere, halfway up a mountain pass, with no neighbours for a kilometre or so in any direction. But who's to say this isn't the centre of the world? I thought. I was reminded of old map makers, long before the whole globe was charted, how they'd often make themselves the centre of the map, whether they were in England, Europe, or Asia. And why not? We are all the centre of our own worlds.

'So,' Dr Mugnier said, 'Do you have any particular health problems?'

Ah.

I looked at my hands. I was thinking; *do I go there?*

But Dr Mugnier had noticed.

'Oui?'

*

Part of the idea of moving to France had been to see if the peace and quiet would make me better, and part of the peace and quiet meant making an end to medical investigations. Back in the UK, the health service had dispensed the best it could, and had concluded its interest in me with Dr Beattie's warm wishes. And just the process of going in and out of hospitals for tests and consultations continually is so very stressful. And on top of all of that, there was still the matter of being ill with something unknown. When you suffer from Undiagnosis, you don't just suffer from the illness, you suffer from the state of not knowing too, and you suffer trying to find the answer that may never come.

So it had been my intention to let medical matters go. To just let the illness be whatever it was, and try to make the best of it. Sure, I couldn't walk very far, there were still very bad days, but there were better spells too, in which I could even do things like cut firewood for five or maybe even ten minutes before exhausting myself. That was the plan. So when Dr M asked if there was anything wrong, I was more than half-tempted to say no, everything was fine.

But he had seen me hesitating.

'There is something?'

'Well,' I said. 'I have been ill for a couple of years.'

'With what?'

I didn't know the French for Chronic Fatigue Syndrome, but I tried the literal approach, *Syndrome de la Fatigue Chronique*.

Dr Mugnier was, momentarily, silent. Then,

'But there is no such illness,' he said, not unkindly, just a little mystified.

I tried using the name ME: myalgic encephalomyelitis, but that didn't make things any clearer. I described my symptoms, how it had all started, and so on. He listened, but could offer no alternative French equivalent to ME, or CFS, and after a little time it became clear that ME simply does not exist in France. Not in the textbook sense, at least.

Does that mean that people in France don't have the condition? That seemed impossible; from everything I knew, ME/CFS is rife in the UK, the US, Europe, worldwide. So, the fact that France doesn't acknowledge that it exists means... what, exactly? It certainly doesn't make you instantly not ill; I had moved to France and my illness had clearly decided to come with me.

What was interesting, to be precise about it, was that Dr Mugnier was not saying that CFS isn't real, or is hysteria of some kind, he had quite simply never heard of it as a concept. And it wasn't just him, I tried the term on a much younger doctor some months later, who I was seeing for something minor and unrelated to the fatigue; with the same result.

I finally found mention of CFS in a French book of alternative medicine, so thought I was wrong about this, but it turned out to be French-Canadian. In France, (at the time of writing) ME/CFS still does not officially exist. There is a movement in France campaigning for the recognition of ME in the country, where it is known by the name 'l'encéphalomyélite myalgique' or EM. As of the date of writing, French health authorities still do not recognise the existence of this disease, despite the fact that the WHO has done so since 1969. The headquarters of the WHO, or the OMS as it's known in France, are in Geneva, less than an hour from where my chat with Dr Mugnier took place.

And this might sound strange, but as it turned out, it was in some ways a good thing that ME does not 'exist' in France, because it meant I came to Dr Mugnier without all the baggage and stigma of disputed illness that it carries in the UK, the USA, and elsewhere. Instead, he simply saw before him a patient with a problem, and resolved to help me. That, in itself, was an enormous relief.

'You are a young man,' he said, and this kind of flattery was entirely acceptable, 'you should be able to walk, enjoy the mountains!'

This sounded right to me; I *ought to be able to walk*; I was still young, in relative terms, or at least in the eyes of my sixty-odd year-old doctor. I thought about the word 'recreation'. Yes, I ought to be able to participate in recreation, not knowing at the time that the original meaning of the word was 'to recover from illness'.*

So I started all over again, and I went through the whole story from Asia onwards. He asked me to come back with all my notes from England, and when I did he pored over them, and finally came to the conclusion that everything had been done that he would have done, save for one thing; I ought to see a neurologist.

I'd explained how the fatigue is worst in the legs, the problems with walking, and he wanted someone to check out my nerves, to see if messages were passing properly from brain to muscle.

---

* The Old French word *recreacion* had this meaning, and a related English word is recorded as far back as the early 15th century; recreate, which in this case was not meant as the sense of re-making something, but rather, to get better through exertion, through exercise. This sense fell away, presumably because of lack of clarity with the modern sense of 're-create', but the term recreation survived. Who today knows that it originally had anything to do with illness?

In 1780 Luigi Galvani, of the beautiful city of Bologna in Italy, made a famous discovery. As the story goes, he and his wife Lucia had been conducting experiments into static electricity by rubbing frog skins. Never a dull moment. One day, as Galvani was doggedly flaying another amphibian for its skin, their assistant accidentally touched the frog with a scalpel that had picked up a static charge: the frog's legs moved; the first recorded account of the phenomenon of bioelectricity.

Before long, Galvani was in a friendly argument with Alessandro Volta about the exact nature of this electrical force, and not long after that, Galvani's nephew, Giovanni Aldini, was continuing to promote his work, as part of which, in London in 1803, he applied an electrical charge to the corpse of a recently executed prisoner, named Forster. The experiment took place at 'Mr Wilson's Anatomical Theatre' in front of an invited crowd of 'professional gentlemen'. These onlookers were shocked, to use the only appropriate word, when the lifeless corpse appeared momentarily to have come back to life, opening an eye, and raising an arm with such force that it clouted somebody in the eye. The arms and legs were made to move, the jaw to clench. While Mary Shelley was only five years old at the time of this experiment, we know that one of the referees of Alessandro Volta's scientific paper on his 'voltaic pile', the surgeon Anthony Carlisle, had told Mary's father William Godwin about this experiment, and it may well have been the model for the passage in her famous book when Victor Frankenstein's creation comes to life and opens his 'dull yellow eye.'

Fast forward two hundred years, and I lay in my underwear on a couch in the hospital down in the valley. The neurologist did not have the same charm as Dr Mugnier, but to compensate for that, he did have a very big set of electrodes. Huge. I had not the slightest worry about this procedure; I had no image of

Frankenstein or Galvani in mind. Then he switched the machine on.

It was torture. With each discharge, and there were ten for each limb, my arm or leg would convulse or kick, and I couldn't believe the pain.

He'd even muttered those infamous words of the doctor – this won't hurt – which as always should have been a giveaway, and yet I'd still expected nothing of this kind. It seemed to last forever, but was maybe only fifteen minutes; all told. When it was over, he told me that everything was normal. No problem with the nerves.

*

Dr Mugnier was at a loss.

I asked him about something I'd been reading a little about; Lyme disease. Lyme is another of those disputed, misunderstood diseases. It's another thing that's very hard to get to the bottom of; that people on both sides accuse the people on the other side of misrepresenting. Borne by the ticks of deer and other animals, Lyme is a bacterial infection caused by a tiny invader known as Borrelia burgdorferi. It's named after the New England town of Old Lyme in Connecticut; a beautiful place.

Since whole books have been written on the controversies surrounding its very existence, largely as to whether its chronic form actually exists, I won't go over all that ground again. Suffice it to say that I wondered whether it was worth testing for it, and various friends had wondered that to me too. At that point, I didn't know that I'd already had a test for it back in England, as part of the huge raft of things they looked for early on. I'd missed it, since it was listed under its Latin name, and there was a lot going on, to say the least. And as I say, there is controversy over which tests are reliable and which are not; it seemed none are 100% certain to give the true picture; there are accusations of false positives, false negatives, doctors who believe you only have it if the site of the original bite develops a certain distinctive 'bull's eye' rash, others who state that only one in two people develop that rash. Or one in three. And so on. Such is Undiagnosis.

Now, Dr Mugnier explained that the French State had decided to investigate the question of Lyme disease since it had become a hot topic, and when the experts reported back they were split 50/50 in their opinion, France as a whole had decided that the chronic form of Lyme disease does not exist.

Oh.

Well, I wondered, what does that mean for someone in France who actually has chronic Lyme? Being told your illness does not exist does not make it go away, and I knew that just over the border in Germany, they believe chronic Lyme *does* exist, and take it very seriously.

*

I was starting to see the edges of the medical realm. When you live in one country, or, to be accurate, when you are only *sick* in one country, it's easy to assume that what you're being told is the very best of medical knowledge as it exists in the world. But what you're actually being told is the current, officially-sanctioned version of medical knowledge in the healthcare system of the country in which you live. You are being told the version of knowledge in that particular centre of the world, and at that particular moment in time. Move to another country, to an edge, which is to say, just another centre of the world, and it's not just that the treatment for certain conditions might vary; whole illnesses simply stop 'existing'.

I was reminded of Resignation Syndrome. This is a mysterious condition afflicting child refugees in Sweden, in which, for two decades, young immigrants have been taking to bed, inert, lifeless, unresponsive. They no longer walk, talk, or even open their eyes in some cases; they are living, and conscious, but effectively comatose to all intents and purposes. It has been the source of huge controversy, and the obvious question which everyone asks is, why does this only affect young immigrants in Sweden, and not elsewhere? The only conclusion most people come to is this: that it's a form of hysteria, what came to be called a Conversion Disorder. Not that the children are faking it, because tell me anyone you know who could fake being in this condition for more than a day or two, but that unconsciously, the children's minds have closed down, unable to bear the separation from their homeland. The idea is then put forward that this response has become 'contagious', spreading to other children in the same position of unbearable pain at being uprooted and moved to a very different culture from the one they know.

In the past, this illness would have been called nostalgia. Another word that we use a bit differently today from in the past, nostalgia derives from Greek words meaning 'homecoming' and 'pain' and was once taken very seriously as an illness afflicting those uprooted from their homelands, rather than as a wistful longing for the past. It was also once known as the 'Swiss disease' since it appeared particularly to affect Swiss mercenaries away fighting in the lowlands; the term nostalgia was coined by Johannes Hofer of Basel in his 1688 dissertation. Symptoms included fainting, fever, stomach problems, fatigue. Apparently, it could even lead to death. The top military physicians explained that the cause was probably damage to the eardrums from the constant clanking of the bells around cow's necks up in the high Alpine pastures. Sometimes, instant cures were witnessed when patients returned home, or were even just *told* they were going to go home.

Though I'd found it helpful, in a paradoxical way, that the illness I'd been told I had in England didn't officially 'exist' in France, it did raise these issues around mass hysterical affliction again; just as with the Swiss Disease, or Resignation Syndrome, if an illness only exists in one part of the world and not in a closely neighbouring one, doesn't that mean it has to be something psychological? Something hysterical, in fact?

No. Of course, there are people with CFS in France; whether it's given a name, or not. My French GP would only go so far as to say that I have an undiagnosed illness, and left it at that; without applying a name to it. The question arises – is that a good thing, or a bad thing? Does it help to be given the label ME or CFS? Back in the UK, one doctor had expressed her satisfaction that I was not the 'kind of person' who would just 'settle into' having the CFS label attached. She told me how some people are, apparently, happy, or at least relieved to be given this so-called diagnosis, and just 'relax' into being ill. That had sounded very unlikely to me, and as the years moved along, I started to believe it was much better not to be given the CFS label. Later, I would speak to three different medical scientists who'd suffered from CFS, and who'd recovered, having finally made their own, accurate diagnoses of rare conditions after years of study. One of them explained to me that once you have the CFS label attached, it's pretty much game over as far as your orthodox doctor is concerned. No further questions will be asked, no further investigations shall be performed, and we'll get to the reasons for that later.

Instead of investigation or treatment, you get this: you have CFS, it's in your head, go away and live with it.

*

But Dr Mugnier was different about it, and he was different for the precise reason that CFS doesn't 'exist' in France, and thus neither do the unwanted stigmas and prejudiced associations that go along with it in the UK and the US.

Maybe you're suffering from homesickness, he suggested. You're living in a foreign land; the language is difficult.

I explained again that I'd been ill for 18 months *before* moving to France; so maybe it's something else, he said.

'I think the problem is psychogenic. In my experience,' he added, 'people are ill for one of four reasons: worry about money, health, relationship or home.'

'Well, I do worry a lot,' I said. 'But I love being here. I don't think living in France is making me ill.'

'Well, perhaps it's something else.'

Yes, I thought, maybe my eardrums have been damaged by the constant clanking of cowbells in the pasture above the house, but I wasn't bitter, or frustrated, as I had been with some of the doctors I'd seen in the UK. Dr Mugnier was kind, charming, funny. He knew I was suffering; he genuinely wanted to do something about it. But here's the thing; just because he had tried harder than Drs T and K back in the UK, and just because he had been more empathetic about the whole thing, in the end, he had still made the same equation that the British doctors had: I don't know what's wrong with you; so it must be your mind doing it. It must be all in your head.

*

Years later, I spoke to Dr Diane O'Leary, a bioethicist and scholar of the controversial area of ME/CFS, about this equation. She was blunt about it; from her office at the Rotman Institute of Philosophy, London, Ontario, she explained that there simply was no rational, scientific, ethical or even remotely justifiable reason of any kind to jump from 'we cannot find what is wrong' to 'therefore your mind is making you sick.' There is no list of diagnostic criteria to make this assumption, for one thing. For another, there had been no studies of whether it would be dangerous to slap a 'psych' label onto people who are very likely physically ill. Whether that was a safe thing to do. As with any other illness, it's clear that stress can make ME/CFS symptoms worse.

'The thing that's really horrifying,' Dr O'Leary told me, 'is that the processes that lead to a diagnosis, if you can call it that, of 'all in your head' have never, ever been tested for medical safety. There is no science there. *None.*'

All this is extremely dangerous stuff, and the real scandal of it is this: in their own ways Dr Mugnier, and Drs T and K back in the UK *would have thought* they were doing the right thing. Dr O'Leary detailed how the field of psychosomatic medicine is a small subset of psych medicine in general; how their papers are generally not peer-reviewed by other medical academics, but only internally, by people who are all motivated to find the same thing, for if they didn't, the edifice of their field of study would crumble, brought to ground if it were to be shown that ME/CFS is not psychosomatic but physiological. Despite this insularity, the instruction that emerges from this little circle is taken by gospel by your family doctor; *even though there is no scientific validity for doing so.*[i]

*

Yet Dr Mugnier was right about one thing – I did want to go home. I was nostalgic for that place. I wanted to go home to the land I lived in before; the land where I was well.

---

[i] For example:
https://docs.wixstatic.com/ugd/23f4ba_ae3ffbf6ff614c669f1e6ad942 0a2dc9.pdf

6 – Learning to Be Someone Else

"Illness is the night-side of life, a more onerous citizenship. Everyone who is born holds dual citizenship, in the kingdom of the well and in the kingdom of the sick. Although we all prefer to use only the good passport, sooner or later each of us is obliged, at least for a spell, to identify ourselves as citizens of that other place."

So wrote Susan Sontag, in her influential essay, *Illness as Metaphor*,[i] the central idea of which is to examine how in language and culture, we use certain illnesses as shorthand for other concepts; so, for example, we might say that crime is a 'cancer' on society. Her short book is rightly lauded as one of the major steps in our cultural conversations around sickness.

Sontag was right about the kingdoms of the well and the sick, but there is an unspoken corollary here: upon occasion, we are obliged to rip up the passport of the land of health entirely; we may never be allowed to return. For some people, born with a congenital illness, the shores upon which one arrives are already those of less-than-perfect health; for others, we are neatly born in the land of the well, but if we're unlucky, may be obliged to make a permanent move to Sontag's kingdom of the sick.

It had become clear early on that there was a possibility that I was never going to recover from this case of Undiagnosis. I'd heard the statistics on the matter; each year, perhaps just 15% of people with CFS get better. Some accounts put the figure at 5%. Yet again, no one really knows. More than that, the life expectancy of people with CFS is lower than for the rest of the population; depending on the cause of death being considered, be it heart disease, cancer or suicide, people with CFS on average live almost 20 years less than people without it. Cancer and suicide show the smallest margin, of about 5 years less, while cardiovascular conditions show a huge margin of 25 years shorter expected lifespan for people with CFS.[ii]

Aside from the numbers, something inside me had told me very early on that I could not feel that it was in my body's power to get well again. This feeling was new to me. I'd always smugly, possibly naively, assumed that I would recover from any illness I might get; now that feeling was absolutely absent. It had just gone. Fans of the it's-all-in-your-head argument might use this to again point to CFS being psychosomatically generated; you see, you really just don't want to get well, you're telling yourself you'll be sick forever. But that is what I felt, and it's hard to say why and when it occurred, but it certainly wasn't there from day one; I think it was a growing feeling in the first six months or so, generated by the frustration and the fear, by the not knowing, by the lack of anything solid to hold onto. By simply being told it was all in your head.

*

It was staring me in the face; I ought to come to terms with the fact that I might never get over this illness, but I couldn't. Not only could I not do that, I didn't want to either. I didn't want to become a person who'd accepted a lesser version of themselves, someone unable to do everything they did before. This was just not acceptable.

Some people could not understand why I was so upset by this. They really didn't see the problem. This is something I've seen again and again when people learn you have CFS – they don't see the problem. This is partially because of the 'but you don't look ill' effect, and partially because the only people who see me at my worst are my family – on days when I am too weak to get out of bed, and lie like a corpse, motionless. This is the nature of 'invisible illness' – we simply do not witness the hundreds of thousands of people who are house or bed-bound. Sometimes, I could only get someone to understand the seriousness of CFS by mentioning the shortened life span; only then would the look on their faces change, and you could see they finally acknowledged having CFS might not be great.

Even then, it didn't always work.

'So you can't walk far, then enjoy being at home.'

'You can still write.'

'Sounds like you've got the perfect excuse to stay in and watch lots of movies every afternoon.'

And then there'd been 'maybe this is the universe sending you what you need.'

Maybe the universe can fuck off, I thought.

I was scared. And I was angry, but it was hard to know who to be angry at, other than 'the universe'. I wanted the old me back, the one who went running, who could hurry all over town from one meeting to the next, who could stay out late at a friend's in the next village and walk tipsily home the mile or so in the small hours. The one who could hike up a mountain.

Every morning, when I woke up, there'd be a tiny, tiny period of maybe just a few seconds in which I'd forget I was ill. I started to feel a little like Guy Pearce's character in *Memento*; Leonard has lost the ability to make short-term memories, and starts off from square one every time he wakes up. Every time I woke up, I went, however briefly, through the shock of remembering I was sick. In those small moments before it kicked in again, I'd think of things I might do, maybe go for a run, maybe I could walk to the next village for lunch and meet friends. And then I'd remember.

Almost worse were the dreams. In my dreams, I was well. I could walk as far as I liked, would run, gave no thought at all to the apparent miracle of standing. And then I'd wake up, and it would all be gone again. With each waking, I would return to the new world, where even to walk across the kitchen was an effort, sometimes a painful one. I had stopped going out for the most part; I might be able to drive into Cambridge, but the walk from the car park to where I wanted to go prevented me. I'd finally asked about getting a blue badge to enable me to park in disabled spaces nearer where I was trying to get to; the doctor told me she knew people permanently in wheelchairs who'd been unable to get them. With this so-called invisible illness, I didn't bother trying.

Along with trying to calculate how many steps I'd have to take if I went out, standing had become a thing I had to think about. Invited to friends for dinner, going to see my daughter in a school concert, I would desperately wait for the invitation to sit down as everyone did the entirely normal thing of standing around for a while first, chatting about the drive and other small talk. Standing for me now had become limited to a period counted in minutes, where before, of course, I never even thought about how long I could stand for; it was simply not something you ever needed to think about. Outside of the home, everything had to be calculated in terms of the steps to the next chair, bench, wall, railing I could sit on until I'd recovered enough to go on; if I didn't, my legs would start to stiffen up at first, and if I pushed on, stabbing pains would start, in the groin, in my thighs.

All this was not a person I wanted to accept. I did not want to become this strange version of me who'd arrived in my body, overnight.

It soon became clear that what this illness was doing was challenging who I was, or who I thought I was. I don't mean this next statement as any supplication for sympathy in some bathetic way, but I have never really liked myself. I genuinely don't mean to make any special plea of woe here, it's just a fact, and I suspect I am, possibly, in the majority of people in this regard. This is not the place to go into generational psychology, but that explosion in the 90s of all those self-help books on self-worth, self-empowerment, and self-affirmation must have happened for a reason – namely, that there was a horrible, yawning feeling inside many of us that we aren't worth anything; that we aren't likeable. Self, self, self. All that 'me-time' stuff. It was supposed to be okay to like yourself, after all, to get what you wanted, what you *deserved*.

But why did you deserve this? I wonder. And as Dr Kristin Neff of the University of Texas, Austin, has pointed out, though the intention of the self-worth movement was good, the result has been very what we now see embodied in what she calls the 'narcissism epidemic' – the ultimate self, self, self movement, furthered all too easily by the last decade's explosion of social media; that thing that can so very easily make us anti-social. It's a fine but important distinction, Neff argues, between self-love and self-acceptance.

Yet despite all that self-love stuff, I was very far from having either of these mindsets; like many people, I liked very little about myself, and the few things that I did like were based on *what I could do*. The thing I was most proud of in life was my determination; once I had decided to do something, I would usually manage to do it, sooner or later. I liked the way I could achieve things, the way I could achieve many different kinds of things. That was how I defined myself, until it was taken away, or a lot of it at least. What was left? Not very much that I appreciated; only one thing that I valued, writing, and even that seemed in danger. I no longer knew who I was, and it seemed very possible that I would have to rip up the passport of my birthland for good.

If that were to be the case, there were, logically speaking, only two options: firstly I could go on being frustrated, depressed, sad and grief stricken, angry at losing myself; or secondly, I could accept it – I could learn to be someone else, someone new. It would still be me, of course, but it would be a new me. I kept coming back to the one big stumbling block with the acceptance route; I just didn't want to be this new person, even if it meant I was happier. I did not want to let go of the past; I wanted to remain me. Whoever I thought that person had been.

*

And yet. And yet. Already something else was happening, a contradiction. Two opposing things were in me, simultaneously. Maybe that should be impossible, or at least some kind of problem, but one of the things about people is that we are able to think two contradictory things at the same time. It makes life confusing, conflicted sometimes, but I think it's something essential to being human. Computers cannot do that. Computers cannot run two incompatible pieces of software at the same time; but people can. It's one of the reasons that I don't believe AI will ever make true works of art, or, I hope to Heaven, write books; those human contradictions are part of what makes us who we are, and how and why we express ourselves in art. If a computer can write a book better than I can, I will expend my last energies on digging a six-foot-deep hole.

Now, I had started to feel something weird; that while, on the one hand, I desperately wanted to be well again, and for all this never to have happened to me, at the very same time, I could begin to see that being ill was changing me. In some very small ways, I had to admit that I liked the person I was being changed into more than the one I was before, the one I was so desperate to return to. It seemed there was, whether I liked it or not, a battle going on in me, over which version of me I was going to be, and which one I wanted to be. Furthermore, it seemed to be a battle over which I had no control; vested in both sides, unable to assist either side to any noticeable extent.

*

As I write this chapter, I have just seen the publication of a novel of mine that features a character who is a retired professor

76

of Philosophy; she likes to quote her field's geniuses to an irritating extent. Dostoyevsky, she points out, though more of a writer than a philosopher, once said 'a man is a being who can get used to anything' and she then goes on to expound Nietzsche's view that 'he who has a why to live, can bear with almost any how.'

There then, that was what I had to do; I had to get used to being something new. I had to learn to be someone else; maybe that in itself was as much of a 'why' – a journey to find out who I really was, irrespective of the person I had thought I was, the person I had defined only in terms of what I could do.

It was not going to be an easy journey. For one thing, I thought, *what else are we* apart from what we do, and what we say? Isn't that how most people define themselves? Is it that terrible to do so?

Jared Lanier, often called the father of Virtual Reality, explains one of the paradoxically interesting things about making trips into non-real worlds. If you imagine yourself in the universe for a moment, and then imagine removing yourself from the universe, what would be left is a you-shaped hole in that universe. The inside surface of that hole is your interface with the universe; we just tend to rarely notice that because we are too busy just being in the world.

When you adopt a different form, as you do in VR when you adopt an avatar, you enter that universe in a new body; it might be a different version of you, still the same sex, although you could change gender; you can even, as Lanier says, become an octopus, a monkey with a tail (and you can learn to use tails or even tentacles in VR), or an alien creature that has never existed. And yet when you travel into the VR world in this new form, you still have the sense of *you*. In fact, he says, somewhat paradoxically, removing your real body from the equation can give you a *stronger* sense of your own self. Travelling to make-believe worlds can give the aware voyager a greater sense of their own identity. Maybe it's not paradoxical at all; maybe the body gets in the way of who we are, most of the time. Maybe it dominates not only how we see others but, critically, how we see ourselves. Maybe it's a good thing to take it away from time to time to get closer to the 'real' us.

When I talk about character in creative writing workshops, I am often prone to embark on a small rant, namely, that personally I find physical character descriptions a bore to write and usually a bore to read. At the start of my career, I argued with my editor for years on book after book where she'd ask for a physical description of the protagonist, for example. It wasn't interesting to me, and rarely do I find it interesting, or necessary, in other's people's books. Yes, we are a visually-dominated species; we are very quick to judge people based on their appearance. We characterise people by their hair-style, their clothes, their skin colour. And when we do, we stereotype. We stereotype characters if we do it in books; we stereotype individuals if we do it in the real world.

Just as in real life, what's interesting about characters in books is rarely the way they look; what's interesting about people is what's on the inside. It's about what they feel, what they think, what they dream of, what they're scared of, what they say when you say the wrong thing to them, how they react when you say the right thing, and so on. That is who you should be trying to get to when you create a character in a book, and that's what we ought to do in the real world, too — see beyond the external to who the person really is on the inside.

So this now was the task before me; to find out, since my body had absconded, to find out who else I might be, without that body to define me; without seeing myself through the constant lens of physicality, the lens of *doing*.

*

For a time, it appeared that 'who else I might be' was an unassuming yet sometimes annoying young German man from Hamburg, taking a trip to Switzerland to see his cousin. In 1907.

[i] Susan Sontag, *Illness as Metaphor*, Farrar, Straus and Giroux, New York, 1978

[ii] McManimen SL, Devendorf AR, Brown AA, Moore BC, Moore JH, Jason LA. Mortality in Patients with Myalgic Encephalomyelitis and Chronic Fatigue Syndrome. Fatigue. 2016;4(4):195-207. doi: 10.1080/21641846.2016.1236588. Epub 2016 Oct 12. PMID: 28070451; PMCID: PMC5218818. doi:10.1080/21641846.2016.1236588

7 – High on The Magic Mountain

'Maybe this is a chance to read all those books you always meant to read,' said another friend. We were working together on a graphic novel. It had been taking years, literally, and I'd phoned up to apologise because – right now – the latest hold-ups were down to me. I hadn't been working at all. Not writing. Not writing, the most terrifying thing of all for a writer, or so we tend to dramatise. So I'd phoned my friend to let him know I had been ill, was still ill, and it had been holding me up.

Since we didn't speak that often, I also took the chance to tell him I'd finally moved to France full time, to live up a mountain. Since he has a French wife and had lived in France for seven years when their boys were young, he knew the appeal. He told me the thing he missed the most was the smell of cheese when you open your fridge.

'So maybe you ought to read Thomas Mann,' Thomas said. 'Given... well...'

'Yes,' I said, 'You're right. I should. I will.'

*

I had always intended to read *The Magic Mountain*. I didn't know much about it, but I'd loved Mann's novella *Death in Venice*, and I had always had a general feeling that I would probably have liked to have read more German literature than the little I had; and for me that meant starting in one of two places; Goethe or Mann. Aside from that, I knew the book was about TB patients in a sanatorium in Switzerland before the First World War, and I knew it contained frequent references to the number seven, and I'm a sucker for that kind of game in a book.

So I read it, and it saved my life, as I will explain below. No small feat that, for a book to save you from dying, but it also did other things for me; not only did it make me question what we mean by 'illness', it also made the arrogance of modern medicine all too plain.

*

As it happens, *The Magic Mountain* has a fair dollop of Goethe in it; Mann's intertextuality ensures that his predecessor is never far from the book's thoughts; even the title derives from a passage in Goethe's *Faust* in which Mephistopheles engages a will-o-the-wisp to guide him and Faust up into the Harz mountains on Walpurgisnacht, that legendary time for witchy-and-generally-magical activity in Germanic legend.

Being chided by Mephistopheles for leading them a zig-zagging route, the spirit replies:

Ich merke wohl, ihr seyd der Herr vom Haus,
Und will mich gern nach euch bequemen.
Allein bedenkt! der Berg ist heute zaubertoll,
Und wenn ein Irrlicht euch die Wege weisen soll,
So müßt ihr's so genau nicht nehmen.

I note it well; you're master of the house,
and I'll comply with your wishes.
But think! The mountain's magic-mad tonight
and if a fairy-light will be your guide,
you mustn't take things too precisely.

You mustn't take things too precisely.

That could be the major theme of *The Magic Mountain*; it's certainly one of them; don't take things too seriously, don't think answers are always exact. Not when what we're talking about is life, and some of the most complex corners of life, such as health and illness. So Mann writes in high ironic style throughout, and though I didn't quite know what to expect from Mann's most famous book, one thing I certainly wasn't expecting is its sense of humour.

Books have been written on Mann's use of irony, and I feel pedantically obliged (sorry) to clarify that here the word 'irony' isn't being used in the way that's in general use now. 'Irony' is used these days to mean some kind of wry cosmic joke – like the fact I had ended up visiting schools as part of my professional life when I'd sworn I'd never step foot in one ever again, or a coincidence of events that evinces some sort of peculiar wince from us. For example, we might be tempted to say something like: "It's ironic that most people think that most of the examples of irony in Alanis Morissette's song *Ironic* aren't good examples of irony, because, in fact, none of them are." But that's not actually what irony is, or what it was originally.

Irony is the effect of the gap between surface meaning and underlying meaning; it is about suggesting a whole lot more than you're saying, maybe even the opposite of what you're saying. It comes in various forms: dramatic irony, tragic irony, sarcasm, litotes and so on, but underneath them all is simply the concept of suggesting something other than the words you have used literally say.

The Magic Mountain is steeped in Mann's dripping irony. He deploys dry and at times caustic irony to tease his characters and make us chuckle; at times, it threatens to belittle them, but it always brings out their humanity and in doing so, it brings us closer to them. It's a sardonically funny book. It's also a sad book, a beautiful book, a moving book. It's wise, knowing, tragic, uplifting, heart-breaking. You can see that I can't say enough good things about it, despite one or two small flaws, and as to those, they need not concern us here. Only Allah is perfect.

It's also a very big book. Generally, I don't like long books. It's true, and I confess that if that makes me a philistine then so be it, though (not) ironically. Until then, my favourite book was a very long one indeed; *Moby Dick*. But then *The Magic Mountain* came along. And I don't theoretically have a problem with long books, it's just that I think that it's rare that a long book needs to be as long as it is.

The plot, such as it is, can be described simply enough. Hans Castorp, an apprentice ship designer from Hamburg, arrives to pay a visit to his cousin Joachim, who's afflicted by tuberculosis and has been dispatched to a sanatorium in Davos, Switzerland. Hans Castorp (with one exception in 700-plus pages, Mann always calls his protagonist by his full name, so as an acolyte, I'll do the same) intends to stay for three weeks; he ends up staying for seven years.

Seven. Mann plays with this magic number throughout the book: it's in seven parts; Hans Castorp's room number is 34; his name, and that of many other major characters are seven letters long and so on. Despite its title, there is almost no 'actual' magic in the book; save for the notable exception of one sub-chapter towards the end of the book featuring a séance. The title alludes more to the notion of being led astray high up here in the mountains, as per the will-o'-the-wisp in *Faust*. Hans Castorp becomes bewitched, enchanted not only by the sanatorium itself and the surrounding mountains, not only by the obscure object of his desire – the infuriating but charming Russian Clavdia Chauchat – but also by the two major doctors in the sanatorium, one of whom rules the body, the other of whom rules the mind.

Dr Behrens is chief-physician, and his medicine is firmly rooted in the body. He reads temperature charts, he pulls eyelids down at the drop of a hat to inspect blood vessels, he uses the latest equipment such as x-ray machines to inspect the state of the lungs of his patients, he counts bacilli on slides and compares them with the notorious 'Gaffky Scale'. If you *do* like physical character descriptions, he's a hefty, powerful man with spades for hands, sometimes described as rowing his way towards people when he walks.

His assistant, Dr Krokowski, on the other hand, is a pallid, yellow-toothed man with pointed beard and whiskers, often portrayed in somewhat devilish terms, and whose realm of affairs is the human mind. Hans Castorp is appalled to learn that he psychoanalyses patients. 'How disgusting!' he declares at first, though a few hundred pages later, he himself later succumbs to the lure of Dr K's psychoanalytical chamber, in a mysterious and obscure series of snippets that beautifully enhance the wonder of our hero's induction into this apparent cult of the mind.

And, at this point, should we be tempted to draw the conclusion that Mann is suggesting that Dr Behrens is the real deal, whereas Dr Krokowski is a charlatan, we have to think again. Ultimately, Mann seems to suggest that both of them are quacks, or maybe that neither of them are; that both are well-intentioned. Again, as the will-o'-the-wisp said, *don't take things too precisely*.

We also ought to remember that much of what seemed to be the hard science surrounding TB later turned out to be as fanciful as any modern-day so-called alternative medicines for the body or flaky therapies for the mind. Things like the Gaffky Scale, which Mann mocks in the book, turned out in real life to indeed be nonsense, for example. We also now know, from restudying their x-rays and other results, that many of the patients sent to TB clinics didn't even have TB; Thomas Mann's wife among them. Katia Mann had been sent to Davos to the very clinic where Mann would later set his novel, known in the book as the International Sanatorium Berghof, nowadays the Waldhotel, Davos. Visiting the hotel a few years ago, the manager explained to me how Katia Mann's case notes had been recently examined; she had never had tuberculosis at all. The underlying reason for her stay there was to recover from the shock and shame of discovering, through the publication of *Death In Venice*, that her husband was homosexual.

*

Another of the themes of the book is how we know if someone is ill. What actually is illness? How can we say someone is ill and when they are well? Where is the border? Underlying several characters' stories in the book is the suggestion that they are not ill *at all*, that they are either malingerers, or in the case of some of the female characters, using illness to get away from bad or loveless marriages and confined gender roles, and live a life of freedom, albeit confined to a Swiss mountainside. There are worse prisons; as Dr Behrens says, it's hardly a Siberian penal colony. But then, each time we start to feel that Mann is pointing us in this cynical direction, someone will drop dead of TB and be whizzed off the premises on a sleigh for a hearse, in the night so as not to upset the other 'guests'. Is Hans Castorp himself ever really ill? Or is he just toying with the idea? It's something that remains unanswered in the book; as it should, since Hans Castorp represents German and more generally European Youth in the pre-war years. The nature of the state of his health, and the struggle to control it by competing parties, is never something that could or should have one simple answer. The only answer Mann gives us is this: ill or not, the war arrives, and that European Youth is sent to fight in the trenches. Illness becomes moot – it is war that triumphs over love, and if that sounds bleak, let me leave you with the last line of the book:

Out of this universal festival of death, out of this extremity of fever, kindling the rain-washed evening sky to a fiery glow, may it be that Love one day shall mount?

May it? Who knows? We, like Mann, can at least hope.

*

After I'd read the novel, reading more about Mann and his life became something else that kept me going. Here was an interesting case, for sure, one whose nationalist political views had ventured away from their original home to a more internationalist stance; a celebrated émigré writer who'd fled Nazi Germany to live in the States. Mann set up home among that small but well-known community of escaped Germans and other Europeans during the war, living in LA, in Pacific Palisades to be precise, of all the incongruous areas in which one could imagine Thomas Mann residing. Reading his letters to and from his friend, another Noble-prize-winning German writer, Hermann Hesse, one thing stands out. They are both sick. Almost all the time. No matter what writing matters they are discussing, what developments in the political world are giving them concern, illness is one thing they always come back to. That started me thinking, again, about whether my being a writer had had any effect on me; was in some smaller or greater way a part of why I had become ill.

'I am sorry your health is not what it should be,' Mann and Hesse repeatedly say to each other. In one letter, Mann assures Hesse that he will no doubt cope, since he is 'experienced and tough'. In another, Mann's ailments include a bad case of a sore throat, neuralgia in the left shoulder, erysipelas (a form of cellulitis caused by bacterial infection), eczema, and a whitlow on his middle finger. He concludes by saying all this has left him in a fit of depression. Ah, but Herr Mann, what would Drs T and K back in Cambridge say? Maybe it's the other way around. Maybe it's the depression that's causing all these ailments. *What would you say*, after all, *if I told you this is all in your head?*

We don't know whether such thoughts occurred to Mann about his own health; if they did, I have found no record. But the notion certainly appears in *The Magic Mountain*. And as I shall mention below, many other writers over time have explicitly laid the blame for sickness at the door of their psyches.

Hesse was not much better physically, plagued by such things as intestinal conditions and eye problems; neither was he in sound health mentally. In 1916, for example, he'd suffered a total nervous breakdown and went to recover in the Sanatorium Sonnmatt, near Lucerne. He took many 'cures' over the years for his mental state, often connected to problems with his writing; in 1921, during the long spell of block he had after completing part one of *Siddhartha*, he took analysis with Jung.

Mann, on the other hand, seems to have been the more repressed of the two when it came to mental health matters. Papers released twenty years after his death showed he had been exclusively homosexual during his twenties, and retreated into marriage after the failure of a homosexual relationship. After this, Mann allowed this side of his nature only to emerge in his fiction, while his diaries record his homosexual yearnings had never left him. He seems to have been of the stock that was made profoundly uncomfortable by the mere thought of un-wellness in the mind, and at the time of course, homosexuality was held to be a perversion. To be ill is an unforgiveable sin? And to be mentally unwell, doubly so, presumably.

Reading the letters and diaries of Mann reminded me of other biographies I'd read, of other writers, with the linking factor being illness. Arthur Ransome, for example, one of my childhood writing heroes, was never a well man. He'd been prevented from enlisting in the First World War due to his flat feet, poor eyesight, and general weak constitution. He suffered huge guilt over the death of his healthy younger brother, who died in the war.

F. Scott Fitzgerald, aside from his alcoholism, was frequently ill; he possibly had tuberculosis, oesophageal varices almost certainly, and suffered two heart attacks in the late 30s before dying of a third in 1940, aged just 44.

Katherine Mansfield, meanwhile, definitely had tuberculosis, and spent the last years of her life seeking ever more obscure, 'revolutionary' cures for it, harming herself in the process.

Commissioned by T.S. Eliot, Virginia Woolf even wrote a monograph about sickness, given her own long acquaintance with it. *On Being Ill*, published in 1926, opens with an impassioned enquiry as to why, given the central, dark power that illness exerts over all our lifetimes sooner or later, illness is not right up there with love, battle and jealousy as one of the prime themes of literature. It's been pointed out that she may just have been wrong about this; although Woolf may not have read *The Magic Mountain*, the epitome of sick books, only first translated to English in 1927 three years after its German publication, there were certainly other significant works focussing on illness by the time of her essay; Tolstoy, Dickens, Defoe had all been there, to name but three notable cases. But perhaps she's right; perhaps these are the few, famous exceptions that prove her general rule that 'literature does its best to maintain that its concern is with the mind; that the body is a sheet of plain glass through which the soul looks straight and clear.'[ii]

*

It's an interesting argument; and sickness in fiction, where it does exist, is most often fleeting, or peripheral. It is something that minor characters deal with; with notable exceptions, rarely are our protagonists sick, and if they are, not for very long. Of course, there are some distinguished books about sickness. Albert Camus' *The Plague*, for example, has been back on many people's nightstands recently, and for good reason. It's a beautiful book, most significantly because it appears to be the work of an author who has not yet given up on the idea that people are fundamentally good (in opposition to the famous line written by his compatriot Jean-Paul Sartre, '*l'enfer, c'est les autres*', from the play *No Exit*).

There are many things to say about Camus' *The Plague*, but notable here is the fact that, albeit a book about the French Algerian town of Oran becoming sealed off from the outside world due to an outbreak of the bubonic plague, the major characters appear immune from the disease. The narrator, Dr Rieux, never succumbs, despite treating many of the dying. Of course, he needs to survive in order to narrate the book, but of all the other eight or so major characters, only one, Joseph Grand, catches the plague, and he makes a recovery. Another, the Jesuit priest Father Paneloux, does die during the book, but it's left open as to whether it's really the plague that's taken him. Some minor characters do die of the disease, of course, and their suffering is truly heart-breaking, as in the case of Jacques Othon, the young son of the magistrate. In a twist, Dr Rieux is separated from his wife throughout the account of the plague because she leaves just as the novel opens to spend some time in a sanatorium, having been unwell for a year. Seemingly spared the risk of one illness by having another, she dies of, it seems, tuberculosis, although she does it offstage as the novel concludes. In general, Camus seems to have known that we do not need to see much suffering directly for the terror of illness to be all too real. And this in a book that stares disease as head-on as any.

And again, another thing to note about *The Plague*, it's author, Albert Camus, was yet another sick writer, yet another with TB. At the age of 17, he was diagnosed as having the illness he would later give his most famous protagonist's wife, thus ending his promising football career as a goalkeeper, and handing him his passport to the notorious world of the sick.

*

So many sick writers. Is this just circumstance? I wondered; maybe these were all just particular cases, but I couldn't help starting to ponder whether there was some connection between being a writer and being ill. I dragged the idea around with me for a while. Tried out various approaches. It could just be, I thought, that everyone was sicker in the old days. Things we can clear up easily now were problematic back then. No antibiotics even, for heaven's sake. A neat dose of penicillin would have licked Mann's erysipelas in no time. Maybe if you read anyone's biography from the early 20th century, you'd read a litany of health complaints; maybe I only ever read about writers and that's why it seems writers are sicker than other people. All those writers with TB? My own grandfather died of TB in 1925, and he was no flaky artist, but a good solid engineer, just as Hans Castorp aspired to be. Still, I could not quite rid myself of the notion, the question: are writers just sick people? Or, here's another thought, do they just complain more loudly about being sick? Or do I just *think* they do, in a classic example of confirmation bias, that classic psychological fallacy in which we only pay attention to things that reinforce the prejudice we already hold?

*

The question of whether the greater part of my illness lay in my head or my body had taken hold of me, infected me as strongly as any disease. I could not get it out of my head, and it came down to a question of whether my mind was making my body sick. Are there really personality types who are more prone to illness, as Dr Beattie had told me?

It appeared instructive to me to think about tuberculosis – given my family connections; not only had my grandfather died of it, my father had had it and recovered as a boy, and given my new found obsession with *The Magic Mountain* – it was a good an example as any of Medicine's changing relationship with certain diseases. To be blunt, with Medicine's mistakes.

Tuberculosis, the disease from which all the 'guests' at the International Sanatorium Berghof are apparently suffering, is not just a disease. It's a history of illness in itself; it's a history of human life and medicine. Just as with ME/CFS, doctors of the 18th and 19th centuries had the same kinds of utterly unproven opinions about the 'kind of person' who succumbed to TB – often contradictory opinions, as it happens, but ones that were firmly believed at the time.

Tuberculosis been around as long as we have; Egyptian mummies dated at over five thousand years have been shown to have signs of the spinal form of the disease; even older, signs of the infection have been found in Neolithic remains in the now-submerged site Atlit Yam off the coast of Israel, and have been dated at around 9,000 years old. Tuberculosis and our understanding of it have advanced together through human history, and though, eventually, following Robert Koch's isolation of *Mycobacterium tuberculosis* towards the end of the 19th century, we have come to understand the illness as a bacterial infection, this enlightenment was preceded by centuries of ignorance, supposition and fear.

Like all the best monsters, what we now call tuberculosis has had many names: it was phthisis to the Greeks; in the Middle Ages tubercular infection of the lymph nodes was known as scrofula, or the King's Evil (this latter name since it was believed that it could be cured by the laying on of hands by royalty); consumption in the eighteenth century, and in the nineteenth, when the name White Plague was also coined. Though (as with scrofula) the bacteria can infect many different body tissues, the most common form is pulmonary tuberculosis, and it is the image of the coughing, wheezing, pale consumptive that still lingers. It may seem like a disease of the past, but nothing could be further from the truth. According to the most recent figures from the World Health Organisation, tuberculosis is the 10th highest of all causes of death worldwide, and the third-highest cause of death by communicable disease.[iii] Tuberculosis has always been an opportunist disease –

today, it has become closely linked with HIV/AIDS, in which it is often tuberculosis invading the weakened immune system that actually causes death.

Despite Mycobacterium tuberculosis being alive and all too well, tuberculosis still is strongly associated with the past, particularly the 18th and 19th centuries, thanks to operas like *La Traviata* and *La Bohème*, paintings such as Christóbal Rojas' *La Miseria*, novels such as *Les Misérables* and *Portrait of a Lady* to name but two books featuring characters dying of 'a consumption'.

I said above that sickness in fiction is relatively a rarity, that it even less often afflicts protagonists. But here we come to the exception that might prove the rule – tuberculosis is different. It somehow achieved an extraordinary thing for any disease to achieve – it became fashionable, it even became desirable, and in doing so, it is the one illness that it seemed acceptable to put front of stage in art.

In real life during the early part of this period, the disease somehow became synonymous with the Romantic poets: John Keats died of it, as had his brother Tom. Percy Bysshe Shelley possibly had it, and even earlier, in 1810, Lord Byron declared that he *wished* he had tuberculosis, as it would make him more attractive to the opposite sex. In this seemingly bizarre remark, we approach the mysterious and paradoxical nature of this chameleon disease. Syphilis didn't do it. Cholera didn't even come close, nor did leprosy. Only tuberculosis somehow managed to make itself a disease that people actually wanted (or thought they did, at least). In fact, literally so. It's been suggested that part of the Victorian fashion for tight corsets was to give women that oh-so-desirable figure of the emaciated consumptive; how chic! Conversely, it was also believed by many medical practitioners in the US, the UK, and France, to name but three places, that the wearing of tight corsets could cause consumption in the first place.

Later, as the role of infection was dimly starting to be understood, women's hem lines were raised to stop them sweeping all the filth of the typical Victorian street into the house. It may seem incredible that any disease could acquire the status of desirability, but this was the case with consumption. One of the most famous victims was Elizabeth Siddal, a poet and painter in her own right but still perhaps best known as the model for many works of the Pre-Raphaelite artists, including her husband, Dante Gabriel Rossetti. Siddal's notorious death, apparently from consumption, and her well-known beauty (somewhat curiously as she was originally selected as a model for her 'plain' features) combined with her having been the muse for such iconic works as John Everett Millais' *Ophelia* and so created an iconic figure to which others wanted to aspire.

How did tuberculosis achieve this miraculous state of being a desirable ailment? In brief, it was down to the ignorance surrounding it. For one thing, it was thought, again paradoxically, that consumptives were both somehow pure and innocent, yet at the same time sexually more active and attractive. It was also thought, with no real rationale at all, that consumptives were more refined human beings, more sensitive, of high intelligence and a generally nervous disposition. Shelley even sympathised with his friend Keats over his illness, and tried to console him by pointing out that "this consumption is a disease particularly fond of people who write such good verses as you have done." All these factors fell slap into the laps of the Romantic image, and behold: a trope was born – the tragic, sensitive, and somehow noble consumptive.

Medical writing at the time was in no doubt about the matter; as late as 1880, Edwin Abalone wrote that:

'the taint of consumption can in many cases be easily recognised by physical signs... The eyes... possess a most remarkable brilliancy...the nervous system is especially developed, hence it is a frequent thing for consumptive patients to be of a most refined nature... being remarkable for the gentleness of their disposition, the amiability of their character, and the great purity of their moral feeling."[iv]

Well, who wouldn't want to be ill with all that?

*

The word for this predisposition to the disease was *diathesis*. Orthodox medical opinion was somewhat confused on the details, but the overall feeling for a couple of centuries or more was that certain 'types' were more likely to get the disease. In the absence of knowledge about routes of infection, this seemed the best explanation for why some members of a household would get consumption, whereas others wouldn't, as opposed to diseases like cholera or the plague that caused open epidemics. And one of the ways in which consumptives made themselves more open to the disease was immoral behaviour. Not usually a specific immoral behaviour, as was the case with the obvious, well-established causes of syphilis, but a more generalised wantonness.

*

So these 18th and 19th-century physicians explored the notion of a tubercular 'diathesis' – the general character, set of personality traits and even jobs which made someone more likely to become 'consumptive'. Entire books were written on the romantic notions of the tubercular – a set of strange and often contradictory ideas about who got 'consumption' and why. It's the idle rich, no, the overworked poor. It's women and effeminate men. It's those with narrow chests, no, it's the disease that makes the chest narrow. But here's the thing – these physicians were all completely wrong.

It's sobering to remember that a *full* understanding and cure for TB only arrived less than a hundred years ago. Equally, much later, Susan Sontag showed in *Illness as Metaphor* how similar bigotry was placed on cancer victims (and still sometimes is). Why is Medicine so quick, so arrogant, to forget its own history? That the idea as the 20th century opened that TB was in some way 'all in the mind' of a certain kind of person, was about to be proved spectacularly wrong? Is not ME/CFS just the latest in a long line of diseases to suffer such bias?

*

I wanted answers to all this, desperately. I couldn't have told you why, then, though now it's clear – I just wanted to know one thing, for sure. It could have been anything, probably, but in the face of all this unknowing, I had become obsessed with finding one thing about illness to which there was an unequivocal answer.

It didn't come.

---

[i] Thomas Mann, *The Magic Mountain*, first English edition, translated by Helen T Lowe-Porter, Alfred Knopf, New York, p900.

[ii] Virginia Woolf, *On Being Ill*, The New Criterion, London, 1926.

[iii] https://www.who.int/news-room/fact-sheets/detail/the-top-10-causes-of-death

[iv] Edwin Abalone, The Cure of Consumption, 1880 6th ed, London, Kemp and Co p24, quoted in Byrne, p28.

8 – Getting Used to
Not Getting Used to It

I said, above, that *The Magic Mountain* saved my life. This is how.

It saved my life because it saved my sanity, which is more or less the same thing, I think; without it, I think that first year or two would have been impossible to survive. In particular, there were two ideas presented in the book that helped me cope; helped me not need to find those answers I desperately craved.

The first was when Settembrini, one of the two major pedagogues who compete for Hans Castorp's attention and spirit, asks the young protagonist how he is acclimatising to life 'up here'.

By 'up here', Mann refers not just to the world of the mountains, of the sanatorium, but the world of sickness in general. The International Sanatorium Berghof represents the real world, too; just as Hans Castorp represents Youth, Mann uses the hospital as a microcosm of Europe before the First World War, symbolising its political dis-ease as much as it refers to literal illness. So when Settembrini asks Hans Castorp if he is getting used to life up here, it's a very loaded question; are you coping with being ill, are you coping with being in a disordered, fractious world, are you coping with not knowing what is going to happen?

Settembrini is impressed with Hans Castorp's answer. Up until this point, the Italian scholar has not given the young German engineer much credit for being anything other than an exemplar of the stout brilliance of the workingman, of the industrious mind, but certainly not for any great academic intelligence or wisdom.

Hans Castorp's answer:

'My cousin Joachim said that many people never got used to it. But one gets used to not getting used to it.'

This strikes Settembrini as extremely witty, and pertinent to boot. He marks up his estimation of his student of life a notch.

Getting used to not getting used to it.

That was something I could get my head around. It was something I could work towards, if I wasn't there already. I felt that it was both honest and true; that it did not evade the pain of being ill constantly, yet did not shoulder one with the burden of having to immediately bear everything with infinite grace as easily as a stoic might wish you to.

Getting used to not getting used to it.

I thought about it a lot, and I needed to. I was thoroughly gripped by depression, and nothing and no one could have been able to get through it, nor did I venture out of it. This simple and yet clever phrase in a book became my lifeline, and whenever I could, I clung to it.

*

Then there was the second idea that Mann's novel made clear for me, something that had been tickling at the edge of my thoughts, but which wasn't coming out since my thoughts were too heavy to allow for anything other than the repetition of my mantra: I'm tired. That thing was a paradox between the mind and the body. There is a paradox in illness, one that had been swimming messily around in my head and which reading *The Magic Mountain* made clear, even though it is not directly expressed therein.

At this point, I must briefly mention the passage in *The Magic Mountain* in which Settembrini, the humanist scholar, declares to Hans Castorp that he hates paradoxes. That he hates paradoxes almost as much as he hates irony, something that's in itself amusing given that Mann is writing a book composed of little else. Mann is having fun with his characters, and enjoying inviting us to the game too, if we want.

This assertion from Settembrini, that he hates paradoxes, comes in response to a conversation he's been having with Hans Castorp. In the book, the pair wrestle several times over the subject of illness, and the nature of the body. It's a rather one-sided wrestling match, since this is intellectual sparring, and certainly at the start of the book Hans Castorp is a six-stone weakling in that department.

Settembrini's views are always hard to pin down; don't take things too precisely, after all, but here's a couple of extracts that give a flavour.

'Humanist – yes, certainly I am a humanist. You could never convict me of ascetic inclinations. I affirm, honour, and love the body, as I protest I affirm, honour, and love form, beauty, freedom, gaiety, the enjoyment of life.'

But a few lines later, he adds:

'However much I dislike hearing that conception of moonshine and cobwebs people call "the soul" played off against the body, yet, within the antithesis of body and mind, the body is the evil, the devilish principle, for the body is nature, and nature – within the sphere, I repeat, of her antagonism to the mind, and to reason – is evil, mystical and evil.'[i]

On more than one occasion, Settembrini rails against the body, even quoting the fact that Plotinus was said to have been ashamed to have had one at all. A body does rather get in the way of intellectual pursuits. How easier it would be to just be pure un-bodied intellect.

In one passage, Settembrini comes as close as we can get to that hoax German expression that illness is a sin. They are discussing the case of a young woman in the sanatorium, Hermine Kleefeld, someone whose motives for remaining ill Settembrini had previously questioned.

'Disease and despair,' he says, 'are often only forms of depravity.'

Hans Castorp is appalled by this notion; here's the passage:

'You are good! Why the girl may lie down and die any day, and you call it depravity! You'll have to make that a little clearer. If you said that illness is sometimes a consequence of depravity, that would at least be sensible.'

'Very sensible indeed!' Settembrini put in. 'My word! So if I stopped at that, you would be satisfied?'

'Or if you said that illness may serve as a pretext for depravity – that would be all right, too.'

'Grazie tanto!'

'But illness as a form of depravity? That is to say, not originating in depravity, but itself depravity? That seems to me a paradox.'[ii]

It is at this use of the word paradox that Settembrini explodes in a rant against their very existence. I'll pass over that to instead talk about depravity.

Depravity. Just as those 18th and 19th-century doctors *knew* that tuberculosis was caused by people's wantonness, Settembrini asserts more or less the same view.

The word used in the German original is *Liederlichkeit*, which German friends tell me means debauchery or dissoluteness: depravity seems a fair translation also, and this is perhaps as close as we can get in literature to the idea that illness is an unforgiveable sin, only beaten by the one place where illness is literally a sin, in Samuel Butler's extraordinary book of 1872, *Erewhon*. *Erewhon* is a dystopian tale of a land where minor illnesses are punished with fines, major ones with floggings or imprisonment. Meanwhile, criminals in the usual sense of the word are taken to hospitals and given understanding and attempts to cure them of their misdemeanours.

*

Begging Signor Settembrini's pardon then; here is the paradox:

Before you get ill, you don't much make the distinction between your mind and your body. Obviously, you are aware that they exist, and that there is possibly some distinction between them, but it is only when one of them fails that you notice how interdependent they are upon each other. In my case, it was only when my body started to fail me that I realised how dependent the mind is upon the body. Physical aches and pains are one thing, but when you cannot think straight, when you lose a sentence halfway through the thought, you see how much the mind requires a body in which to exist. Illness had showed me how interconnected the two things are, and yet the paradox is that, at the very same time, the distinction between the mind and the body had never been greater, the gulf never wider.

When well, we can easily ignore our bodies; we can push them, overuse them, treat them badly, and we know without even having to think about it that they will recover. Our mind is free of the body. Only when they break down are we made to powerfully associate mind and body; we see that they are inseparable, yet now they have never felt more apart.

The thought-experiment of becoming something else in virtual reality; only when we remove the body can we approach what is truly *us*. And yet we never get to cast off the body, save perhaps in dreams, and now for the first time in human history, users of VR get a glimpse of it. Does illness force you to engage the same question; to see who you really are, without your physical self, and your actions, to define you? Virginia Woolf would have recognised this struggle. The body is a sheet of plain glass through which the soul looks straight and clear? Nonsense, she says, in *On Being Ill*; "All day, all night, the body intervenes; blunts or sharpens, colours or discolours..."

In other words, how do we ever see the mind without the body? And yet, being ill, how separate the two aspects of us have become.

So I sat on my own mountain, about eighteen months into being ill, and if it was not quite as magic as the one in Mann's book, it nevertheless enchanted me, just as I was in turn enchanted by his great novel. This feeling of seeing my mind and body separating yet simultaneously reinforcing their relationship with each other was curious, and whilst frustrating, it set me thinking about things I suspected it was high time I thought about.

Because, for all the good that *The Magic Mountain* did me, it also poured water on another seed that had been growing at the dark corner of my mind. A view that perhaps my illness came from somewhere else, somewhere I really didn't want to go. A view expounded by Herr Dr Krokowski in the International Sanatorium Berghof. A day or so into his arrival on the mountain, Hans Castorp learns that the good doctor of the mind gives bi-weekly lectures to all guests of the establishment, and that all patients are invited (by which is meant expected) to attend. On the Monday, our young Hamburger duly turns up at the first lecture, a little late, having taken it into his head to go for a hike beforehand. He's got carried away and has pushed himself too far in the thin air, has suffered a nosebleed and arrives with stains down his shirt, and his head still swimming. There, he sits in the row behind the deliciously yet annoyingly captivating Clavdia, and is mostly distracted from what Dr K is saying by making half-desirous, half-derisive remarks to himself about her arms, or the lace of her sleeves, or the way she fondles the hair at the back of her neck. That is, until Dr K starts in on the central argument of his lecture; that all illness, all of it, is a transformed, thwarted emotion; and not just any emotion, but one in particular; and that, Dr Krokowski intones, as everybody in the room leans eagerly forward to find out the cause of all their suffering and pain, that emotion, that thwarted desire, is none other than... Love.

Reading this, I too leant forward, in discomfort, for these were not words I wanted to hear, even in fiction. *Especially* in fiction, which is so powerful that it ought to be banned, and therefore sometimes is. Was I ill because my private life had been a series of broken dreams?

---

[i] Thomas Mann, *The Magic Mountain*, first English edition, translated by Helen T Lowe-Porter, Alfred Knopf, New York, p 317.
[ii] Thomas Mann, *The Magic Mountain*, first English edition, translated by Helen T Lowe-Porter, Alfred Knopf, New York p 282.

9 – The Sun Will Go Out

'You're too sensitive,' said everyone, frequently.

I'd heard it most from girlfriends, but from others too. From friends, from work colleagues, from bosses, from family, from teachers. Throughout my life, I had this accusation levelled at me; *you are just too sensitive.* Try to feel things a little less deeply; it'll be easier for you. And us.

Assuming I had even wanted to, can you simply just decide to feel things less deeply? Isn't that like telling someone to be taller than they are, or change their skin colour? Maybe not; the relatively new field of neuroplasticity shows that with sufficient effort, we can train our minds to work differently from their habitual manner; but as a young man, I didn't think about being less sensitive, let alone try. And when I finally did think about it, I realised something.

Some years ago, I had a minor epiphany during a creative writing retreat. This was a different one from the one with the GD, one long before I got sick. It wasn't possibly the most professional thing, but at least it was authentic in the moment when it came to me. I was speaking to the assembled writers about the need to connect with what moves you in order to write powerfully, and that I had had enough of apologising for being sensitive. I'd felt guilty about it all my adult life, had been told it caused problems in all sorts of relationships. Enough, I declared. We are writers *because* we're sensitive. So there! We feel things; we feel moved to try to make sense of them; in order to do that, we assemble stories from them. We should be celebrating our sensitivity, not apologising for it. Not running from it.

Within the world of books, you often come across the opinion that writers must have very thick skins to cope with the criticism, to even be able to expose their work (which is more personal than many realise) to the scrutiny of an editor, a publisher, and ultimately maybe a reading public. Perhaps worst of all, to critics. The reverse is true: every writer I know to any degree at all has a very *thin* skin; some are just good at hiding it behind diffidence, arrogance or other smokescreens. It was said of Lord Byron, for example, that he was completely *skinless* in regard to criticism; after his first published work was roundly savaged in the *Edinburgh Review*, he drank three bottles and threatened to shoot himself in the head. Finally, he contented himself with revenge in ink, writing a long riposte in verse, *English Bards and Scottish Reviewers*, that not only crucified the editors of the magazine, but managed also to slay notables such as Walter Scott, Coleridge, and Wordsworth for good measure.

So, henceforth, I determined I was not going to be ashamed of being sensitive. It's facile but probably therefore true that this shame had begun at that Grammar School, where they tried to toughen us sensitive kids up with all that 'character-building' stuff; but as I said before, it didn't work. If you're sensitive, those abuses passed off as character building are like being flayed alive; you might end up with some pretty hard scars on the outside, but you'll be more fragile than ever on the inside.

Sensitive. It's another word that has changed its meaning over the years. There are few that haven't. Originally, going as far back as we can, it stems from the Latin *sentire*, meaning to feel or perceive. In Medieval Latin, this gave us *sensitivus*, again simply meaning capable of sensation. In Old French, this became *sensitif*, which is retained in Modern French in anatomy and physiology. And all these variants simply mean that ability to feel or perceive something. There is no connotation of weakness, no pejorative sense here. For that, we need to wind into the early 19th century English usage where we get the first recorded instance of sensitive meaning 'easily affected mentally.'

It's probably too late now, but it would be nice to think we can reclaim this adjective and strip it of the negative connotations. For who now uses *sensitive* in a neutral manner, let alone a positive one? Perhaps the word only has negative connotations in relation to the world it now lives in. Along with all that self-love stuff that kicked off in the 90s, we were also supposed to celebrating another message from the 80s onwards, that of the importance of making the individual sacrosanct, to place the individual above society, to be tough, to be 'me-first'. No place in there for sensitivity; because nice guys finish last, right? So maybe it isn't the word that changed, maybe the world changed around it. It tried to go on holding its meaning, but the enclosing world came to despise it. The very same history can be seen in the word *pathetic* – a word which once simply meant something like 'capable of arousing feelings'; it has similarly come to mean something explicitly negative and weak.

At the risk of sounding fanciful, I had always felt that not only did I seem to be more mentally sensitive than some (at least, people kept telling me I was), but I also felt more physically sensitive; to heat, to pain, to pleasure, to food. It was as if I had a body made by whoever made the amps in Spinal Tap; everything went up to eleven. More nerve endings than in most people was how a friend of mine once put it. Now I had become sick, with something that was hard to pin down, and was maybe in my head and was maybe in my body, and I wondered: is this just happening to me because I am feeble? Am I just a weak person? Too sensitive in every way?

*

It reminded me of the tubercular diathesis again; that being ill is somehow down to you: your nature and behaviour; that it was your fault. In her book *Tuberculosis and the Victorian Literary Imagination*, Katherine Byrne notes that the discovery of the

Mycobacterium bacillus did not, paradoxically, initially kill the idea of the consumptive diathesis, as it ought to have done:

'It was known that the tuberculosis bacillus could enter the body and have no effect, for post-mortems had often revealed old, healed tubercle deposits in individuals who had lived healthy lives and died of unrelated illnesses. This shifted the emphasis back to the individual, for if the bacillus did not automatically cause disease, then those who succumbed to it were, it seemed, in some way responsible for their own illness.'[i]

It's only a little over a century since we treated people dying of tuberculosis in this way. Ever since I'd read *The Magic Mountain*, I had had the feeling that that we're now just in the same mode of thinking with ME/CFS, and while this illness may not be life-threatening, it is both life-changing and statistically life-shortening. It really doesn't help to be told it's your fault that you're sick; in fact, it's just one more burden that the illness has brought to you. Something in the way you're made; something wrong with your thinking.

This feeling is present not only in fiction – witness Dr Krokowski in *The Magic Mountain* and his lecture on all illness being thwarted love – but in history too: writers are particularly prone to ascribing their physical ailments to their mental state, matters of love in particular. In *Illness and Metaphor,* Susan Sontag discussed the way in which two diseases, in particular, have been used metaphorically to discuss other aspects of society, above all others: cancer and, before that, tuberculosis. Sontag wrote the long-form essay shortly after surviving breast cancer in 1975, obviously placing that illness at the forefront of her mind. She presumably chose TB as the other focus of the piece for a variety of reasons, not least that she, before me, was someone else greatly enamoured with Thomas Mann's masterwork. (Many, many years after the event, she wrote a beautiful account of how she, and her best friend Merrill, decided one day to pay Herr Mann a visit in his home in Pacific Palisades. In fact, it was Merrill's idea and she was horrified, but went along and met her great hero. She was still only fourteen years old, hugely precocious, longing for a life that believed books and art to be vital necessities, a life she could not find in her own family home. It's an utterly mesmerising account of the slightly awkward encounter of two cultures, two ages, two generations. It's called *Pilgrimage*.)

*

In *Illness as Metaphor*, Sontag enumerates many cases of sick people who believed that their illness was their own doing; something wrong in their head:

Katherine Mansfield, convinced that her tuberculosis had its origin in her soul: "the weakness was not only physical. I must heal my Self before I will be well. It is at the root of my not getting better. My mind is not controlled." This was a year before tuberculosis killed her, having undergone radical 'cures' such as an x-ray treatment on her spleen, which left her with heat flashes and numb legs.

And here's Franz Kafka to Milena Jesenská, with whom he had a very brief affair: "I'm mentally ill, the disease of the lungs is nothing but an overflowing of my mental disease." This four years before his death from TB, having come to the belief that "tuberculosis... is no special disease, or not a disease that deserves a special name, but only the germ of death itself, intensified..."

Making the connection to love totally explicit, John Keats, knowing he would probably never see his fiancée Fanny Brawne again, wrote to a friend, "I should have had her when I was in health, and I should have remained well." He died less than four months later, believing that if only he had got his heart's desire, he would not have become ill. That, in effect, he died of a broken heart. At least, as his friend Shelley had pointed out to him, there were advantages to being ill, specifically to having TB.

Sontag shows how the supposed link between illness and creativity, if it were not there before, was firmly established by the Romantics. In 1810, Byron was on his particularly Levantine Grand Tour, and spent some time with an old college friend, the Marquis of Sligo.

After a bout of fever had laid him low for a few days, and caused him to lose some weight (about which he was very touchy about), he stood in front of the mirror one day, then turned to Lord Sligo.

According to his friend and biographer, Tom Moore, Byron said:

"How pale I look! – I should like, I think, to die of a consumption."

"Why?" asked his friend (who was himself actually tubercular).

"Because the ladies would all say, 'Look at that poor Byron, how interesting he looks in dying.'"

Similarly, Lady Caroline Lamb, writing of Glenarvon, her fictional cipher for Lord Byron with whom she had had a passionate but brief affair, wrote how the mysterious young lord was received into Society 'with more than common civility: his ill state of health, his youth, his beauty were powerful attractions.'

To be tubercular was the original 'pale and interesting' – never mind illness as metaphor, here is illness as cosmetics.

'Sadness made one "interesting"', notes Sontag. And disease doubly so, presumably. She expands on where that belief takes you; 'but it takes a sensitive person to feel such sadness; or, by implication, to contract tuberculosis.'

According to this Romantic view, it takes a sensitive person to be ill.

*

Tuberculosis was a disease particularly associated with love and sexuality. It's an extraordinary thing for a disease to have achieved, but consumption actually became something people wanted. Or thought they did. While the actual 'diseases of love', or 'diseases of Venus' – venereal diseases – were clearly a product of depraved activity such as consorting with prostitutes and having affairs, and as such had obvious even if poorly understood vectors of transmission, nothing accurate was known about tuberculosis at all. But that didn't stop there being plenty of inaccurate suppositions about it. It was thought that it caused fits of heightened sexual awareness and activity; the periodic red flush of the otherwise pallid cheeks was taken as a sign of health – disease as cosmetics. It was also taken to be a sign of wantonness; the tubercular were believed to not only be more attractive, but to have greater sexual hunger too. One characteristic trait of late-stage tuberculosis, a thing known to the medical world as *spes phthisica*, in which the victim suddenly experienced a final burst of passionate energy before expiring for good, probably added to this notion.

This link between consumption and passion has old roots – Shakespeare's *Much Ado About Nothing* contains a joke between Beatrice and Benedict about how she will have to love him to save him from 'a consumption'. How far back this link goes, we cannot be sure, but by the time the Romantics got hold of it, it was firmly established. For the Romantics, particularly the poets, this link between love and illness was, quite simply, fact. As was the link with both these things and creativity.

*

Poets even more than prose writers? Virginia Woolf explains why in *On Being Ill*. Speaking of how we react when we take to our sick beds: "It is to the poets that we turn. Illness makes us disinclined for the long campaigns that prose exacts." Maybe so, and maybe too, those fat novels are just too weighty to hold up for long periods when you're weak.

How the world changes for us when we become ill! Woolf says. In an extraordinarily poetic, dream-like flight of prose writing, she explores the changed world of the bed-ridden.

"There is, let us confess it (and illness is the great confessional) a childish outspokenness in illness; things are said, truths blurted out, which the cautious respectability of health conceals. About sympathy for example; we can do without it. That illusion of a world so shaped that it echoes every groan, of human beings so tied together by common needs and fears that a twitch at one wrist jerks another, where however strange your experience other people have had it too, where however far you travel in your own mind someone has been there before you – is all an illusion. We do not know our own souls, let alone the souls of others. Human beings do not go hand in hand the whole stretch of the way. There is a virgin forest, tangled, pathless, in each; a snow field where even the print of birds' feet is unknown. Here we go alone, and like it better so. Always to have sympathy, always to be accompanied, always to be understood would be intolerable. But in health the genial pretence must be kept up and the effort renewed – to communicate, to civilise, to share, to cultivate the desert, educate the native, to work by day together and by night to sport. In illness this make-believe ceases. Directly the bed is called for, or, sunk deep along pillows in one chair, we raise our feet even an inch above the ground on another, we cease to be soldiers in the army of the upright; we become deserters."

Even this long quote is a brief extract of a bitterly felt, utterly personal set of pages in her essay, and I think it's worth reading over and again. It was certainly a passage that meant something to me when I first read it; to me, she captured so well the way in which illness isolates, differentiates, segregates.

Life changes when you become ill; people change, things change, because their meaning changes. And though Woolf doesn't say it explicitly, one of the things that changes when you're ill is you.

"It is only the recumbent who know what, after all, nature is at no pains to conceal – that she in the end will conquer; the heat will leave the world; stiff with frost we shall cease to drag our feet about the fields; ice will lie thick upon factory and engine; the sun will go out."

Oh my.

It is only the sick, Woolf argues, who are being honest; only the sick who can see, and accept, the meaningless of life, of all that striving, striving, striving that the healthy seem so busily, if ultimately pointlessly, occupied with.

This is, we have to admit, bleak.

*

But maybe, I thought, as I moved on through the second year of illness, that's just because writers are too sensitive, it's only those spineless, weak-kneed, feeble and frail snowflakes who think this kind of thing. That's an argument. It's a pretty simplistic one, but maybe we ought to give it the time of day anyway, so here it is: writers are 'pathetic'.

On the other hand, maybe they are the only ones who are strong enough to actually look at the ultimately pointless bleakness of the world and face it head on; stare into the abyss, etc, etc, blah, blah, yawn. Perhaps it's Woolf's busy 'Mrs Jones' and 'Mr Smith', as she names them, who are really the weak ones; too weak to even contemplate the innate terror of the universe in which ultimately, as Woolf bluntly points out, the sun will be extinguished.

What this passage in her essay captures above everything else, however, is the sense of isolation that illness brings, and to that I'll return later.

Meanwhile, type 'author' or 'writer' into your favourite image search engine. The Internet is bad at subtlety, but it's great at stereotype. So the results, as offered to us by the crowd-mind of the web, should provide you with a pretty good picture of the stereotype of a writer. I am guessing that if you've just done this, you're now looking at a picture of someone with spectacles. Probably someone thin, certainly not corpulent, certainly not muscular. (Probably someone white and male too, but that's a story for another time). But stereotypes are *sometimes* stereotypes for a reason; the cliché is sometimes a cliché because it's the overused truth. So is this the writer; frail, weak, overly thoughtful? A worrier, too, I'll wager.

Maybe, maybe, maybe. I wanted some answers to all these maybes, but it would be some time before I started trying to find out if it's actually true that writers are frailer than most people; both mentally and physically. For now, I was still wrapped up by the question of whether my particular illness was mental, 'in my head', or physical, 'in my body'.

I'm sure more than one person reading this book will have many pages ago wondered if I would ever get to the very debatable issue of the mind/body distinction, and here we are. To the doctors who would have it that my illness was all in my head, and to me and other less orthodox doctors who believed that the problem is all in my body; there is – of course – the third way, a unified position, which ought to be where we start, but isn't. The mind is the body and the body is the mind, and we cannot separate them, nor place where illness lies in them, as if in distinct lands.

The reasons why this is not the starting place of most modern 'Western' medicine are long, historical and economic. The fact is, most medicine comes from the one camp, or the other, but there are a few rare people who dare to suggest that a more holistic, integrated view is in order, and I would meet some of those people before too much longer.

*

Meanwhile, meanwhile, I settled into life in France. I didn't get better, but the views were good while I read my books, and the wine was indeed cheaper. I started to write again, and wrote a long novel, with a complex plot, one that reassured me my mental faculties were not entirely dead yet. I continued to investigate ways in which I might get better, and then one day, two and a half years into being ill, I got the opportunity to go and play Hans Castorp myself for a while. Not for seven years, it's true. Just two weeks. Two very interesting weeks, as it happened, during which I did not eat a single thing.

---

i Katherine Byrne, *Tuberculosis and the Victorian Literary Imagination, CUP, Cambridge,* 2011, p24.

10 – Hunger

'He won,' Herr Direktor said.

I had only just met Herr Direktor; I had no idea if Herr Direktor had a sense of humour or not.

'You're joking,' I said.

It appeared Herr Direktor did not have a sense of humour, not that morning, anyway, and with very good reason.

'You're not joking?' I said.

He shook his head, and struggled to make eye contact.

*

I'd only arrived at the clinic overlooking Lake Constance the afternoon before; it had all been a bit of a whirlwind, and at nine o'clock the following morning, here I was in the director's office, to conduct an interview as part of my stay.

'The final results are still coming in, but there's no doubt. He's won.'

So, there it was; the confirmation of the start of the end of the civilised world. Herr Direktor was clearly in shock, and now I was too. It was a strange way to meet someone, a strange but suddenly intimate way to bond with a stranger; we might agree on nothing else, but we suddenly connected over the horror that was unfolding in America.

Herr Direktor was still struggling to make eye contact; perhaps a little awkward at seeming momentarily unprofessional with someone who'd come to interview him. I wanted to do something. I wanted to reach out and tell him I shared his concern, that he could say what he wanted, that sometimes being professional doesn't matter. I didn't. My eyes fell where his gaze was landing, in a vague, unfocussed way. There were five little statues on a table at the side of his office. Plastic figurines, slightly different sizes, each a few inches tall, coloured. I looked at them closely.

'Are they...' I looked more closely. 'Are they... you?'

A friend has a 3D printer, he explained.

'Oh,' I said. 'They're very accurate.'

Is Herr Direktor a little narcissistic? I wondered. One 3D printed statuette of yourself in your office maybe... but *five*? But then compared with the mirror-shattering, megalomaniac, infantile narcissist who'd just been elected as leader of the free world, five little plastic figures seemed just what they were; mostly harmless.

Herr Direktor shook himself.

'How are you finding things, so far? Please, sit down.'

Relieved at the invitation at last, I sat.

'Very nice,' I assured him. 'I've been well looked after. Doris gave me my welcome tour.'

'Ah, Doris! She's wonderful,' he said, smiling warmly at the thought of the maternal type on reception who had shown me around the evening before. He consulted a sheet in front of him. 'And Herr Dr Wittrock will be your physician while you stay with us. He is excellent. He is the most...' He searched for the right word '...precise of our doctors. Very clear with his science. Lots of blood work! Oh, but perhaps you have only come to write this article about us?'

I'd been asked, by a happy coincidence, to travel to Germany and write a piece for a British magazine about this health clinic. The coincidence was happy since I had already been reading about similar places, and had been wondering whether what they offered might be the miracle cure that I was looking for. The place I'd come to was not just another expensive private health clinic; a super-spa for the idle rich. No, there something very particular about this place; it had a treatment program based around a simple, and apparently very powerful, tool; that starving yourself for a couple of weeks or so could heal you. Of almost anything.

'No, no,' I assured Herr Direktor. 'Of course, I'm here to write the article, but as it happens I do have some health problems of my own.'

'Ah! Excellent,' he exclaimed, adding, 'I mean, not excellent, but I am glad you will get to see our approach to health at first hand. I wish you an excellent fast.'

*

The clinic was a family-owned business, with a history going back several decades – the founder had cured himself of severe rheumatoid arthritis, so severe that he was confined to a wheelchair. Following the prompting of his own doctor, he had fasted for 19 days, at the end of which his arthritis was gone. He went on to establish the clinic that bears his name today, when more orthodox science is starting to catch up with the idea of fasting as a therapy. In the last few years, work by people such as Dr Valter Longo of USC, and earlier, Japanese cell biologist Yoshinori Ohsumi had demonstrated that periodic fasting has proven health benefits; it appears that it 'reboots' the immune system by the eradication of old, weak white blood cells and the creation of new ones.

Autophagy, literally 'eating yourself', is the process through which this happens, as your body switches to living off reserves it has previously laid down in your body. More and more studies were being published proving its efficacy. Ohsumi had won a Nobel prize for his work; that was good enough for me, and I wanted to try it.

Now it had crossed my mind, of course, that you could just stop eating at home; why pay all this money for places like this clinic were charging (and the fees are considerable) to have someone not feed you? So when I'd first heard about it, I'd tried fasting at home; I got to almost exactly 48 hours, with no trouble at all. Then I felt something kick inside me, some absolutely primal urge, and I went and emptied the entire fridge, joining my family for Sunday dinner. It had seemed so easy up to that point, but maybe it was just too hard sitting in the living room for two days, whilst others were enjoying their meals as normal.

At the time, the research seemed to suggest that it took at least 48 hours, but maybe 72, for the autophagy process to switch in. Maybe I would need to try for longer, since I had felt no real benefit from my two-day fast. Just as I was wondering whether I might manage to make it to three days on another try, the invitation came to go to Germany and do the real thing; go the whole hog. Or rather, no hog at all. The best part was that all of my stay, and all of my treatments, would be paid for, in return for something easy enough for me to produce: an article for a magazine. So off I went.

*

It really was just like the International Sanatorium Berghof up on Mann's magical mountain; the clinic was a melting pot of populations; many Germans, of course, lots of French, one or two English, a few Americans, sprinklings of other nationalities. There were lectures and evening entertainments. There was *die liegekur*, the legendary rest-cure of TB sanatoria, in which you lie on a balcony in the sun, swaddled in blankets.

There was only one topic of conversation for the next couple of days. Should anyone outside America be in any doubt as to the awareness of the rest of world for their country, or the concerns and effects the USA places on non-US shores, the mood in the clinic would clarify the matter. I commiserated with the Americans, more than one of whom felt the need to apologise on behalf of their country; I argued with three French businessmen who told me that 'democracy had spoken', but were utterly unaware of issues of voter registration, selective closure of polling booths, and possible Russian interference, all of which were known about even then. I sat in the sauna with a very large Turkish man who spoke no English, but just muttered one word; the name of the new President elect, and grimaced. I grimaced back.

Otherwise, I got on with the business of not eating.

*

It was really very simple. You do not eat for two weeks. Or three, if you're going for the 'classic' cure. I exaggerate slightly. Of the two weeks, the first day was spent in 'digestive transit'. This means, in order to acclimatise your gut for what's about to hit it (or rather, not hit it), you eat just one type of food for the first 24 hours: rice, fruit, or vegetables, and in very modest amounts. I opted for rice, thinking it the least potentially explosive choice. During the final three days of the fast, food is reintroduced very gradually, so as not to overwhelm the gut again with the shock of starting to eat once more.

So it was on the second day that the not eating really started.

I have to admit, I was apprehensive, to say the least. I have always been someone prone to those sudden sugar-level drops that leave the hands and legs shaking and the mind ravenous, and the modern portmanteau 'hangry' is something I'd been familiar with long before someone made up a good word for it.

Part of the reason for spending a lot of money not to eat, in fact, a very large part of it, is to do it somewhere 'safe' – with medical staff on hand should you have any problems. Perhaps even more fundamentally, it is to be surrounded by other people doing the same seemingly insane thing that you're doing. And not just the guests; upon settling me in, Doris had told me how the vast majority of the staff, herself included, would undertake a fast at least once a year, convinced of the health benefits. At the end of the tour, she'd shown me around my room, which being the geek I am, I was delighted to see was 214, because like Hans Castorp's number 34, the digits added to seven.

'This is the bathroom,' she said, in that redundant but polite way that upmarket hotels insist upon. 'And here's your iPad. There's a short video to watch each day to explain what will happen. Please sign this contract for its use.'

I signed.

'And here is your bed. It is here that you will take the liver compress every other day, alternating with the colonic irrigation.'

'Yes, I see,' I said.

She smiled.

'For many people, this really is the highlight of the stay.'

Her eyes twinkled in the way that the eyes of cult members twinkle.

'Oh,' I said. 'I, err, see.'

I was, I admitted to myself, apprehensive. Worried? Maybe a little, but here I was, surrounded by people not eating, and no one seemed to be dying.

'The human body can survive for 37 days without food,' Doris assured me.

It seemed a very precise number, but maybe she'd been speaking to precise Herr Dr Wittrock, whom I had yet to meet.

'Yes, yes,' I said. '37. I see.'

'If you have any queries at all, please phone reception. For any medical concerns, you can call one of the nurses; their station is just on the floor above you. Have an excellent fast.'

Doris left. The following morning day I interviewed Herr Direktor; material for my article. And then... Then there was... nothing.

*

The very first thing you notice when you stop eating is this; you suddenly have a fuck of a lot of extra time in your day. Eating takes ages... preparing food to eat even longer. Which is why, for many people in the industrialised Western world, food has become a pre-prepared, pre-processed thing you eat on the run, at your desk, in the car, standing in line, wherever... Even an evening meal at home is very possibly something bought from a take-away, or emptied out of a sealed plastic container. The rush of much of the modern world has led us to rush and cheapen and degrade perhaps the single most important thing in our lives; the food we eat.*

*

Suddenly, for the best part of two weeks, that whole equation of food and time was gone. With one small exception; every evening at six, the entire guest population of the clinic would meet in the communal room upstairs in the main building for a nourishing glass of fruit juice. A *small* glass of fruit juice. A small glass of *weak* fruit juice. That was it; that was the only thing that

----

* A couple of years later, writing another travel piece about a similar but if anything even swankier clinic, another doctor suddenly became a Marxist of the Frankfurt school in front of me as he launched into a critical analysis of the entire food industry.

'And "industry" is what's at the heart of the matter,' he told me, as he explained how the invention of snack food, so heavily marketed and advertised to us for the last few decades, along with the use of high-fructose corn syrup as a sweetener in almost everything and anything, had led to the diabetes epidemic sweeping America and Western Europe.

'The body needs time between eating. Even overnight is a small but important fast; and the longer you can go between your evening meal and breakfast, the better. The body needs to rest between eating; with constant snacking, which we have been sold in order to make the food industry more money, the level of insulin never drops. This is what's causing the explosion not just of diabetes but many more health issues.' Then he stopped being a Marxist of the Frankfurt school and became merely a German doctor in a Bavarian health clinic once more.

was to pass my lips for the next ten days, aside from the litres of water you need to drink to get you through, and the mineral mix to stop you from getting sick from an imbalance of body salts.

If I was in for a shock with this whole not-eating thing, I got one: it was very, very easy. Too easy. Ridiculously easy. Something in me felt I really ought to be suffering in some way, but I just wasn't. I kept waiting to be hungry, for the blood-sugar drop to kick in, for the moment when I started trying to boil and eat my slippers as Charlie Chaplin did with his shoes in *The Gold Rush*; or I would look at one of the nurses and see her turn into a roast chicken, like Wile E. Coyote gazing upon Road Runner, but none of this happened.

At my first check-up with the nurse, I wondered aloud about it.

The reason it's easy, Suzanna explained, was down to the laxative salts I'd been given on the first morning.

'Once the gut is empty,' she said, 'it closes down. Shuts up shop. It doesn't feel hungry after that.'

Yes, I remembered Doris had said something similar the day before.

'Just as long as you drink enough water, and take the minerals, you'll be fine.'

I remembered that too. Drink at least two litres of water every day. Three if you can manage it. They'd also explained how on the second or third day, one might feel a little rough; the result of the body taking the chance to finally expel all the toxins you'd been putting into it. Once this phase was over, then came the pay off – a sudden rush and burst of energy like you hadn't felt in years. At this stage, people would rush out for long walks, do double sessions in the gym, lift cars single-handedly, and so on. I would have been happy if I could just walk from the block where my room was to the main building without my legs feeling like trash, and I waited hopefully for that to happen.

On day two, in the evening, I had my worst detox moment: a mild headache for an hour or two. That was all, and I wasn't even sure it was detox, and not the bright lights overhead in the meeting room where we were sitting. On day three, a small commotion: a woman 'had a turn' during one of the evening lectures. It turned out she hadn't been drinking the supplies of water placed in her room on a daily basis. Ah yes, a few of us noted to each other with raised eyebrows, as if we were seasoned veterans of this business, you have to drink enough water.

But was I hungry? No, not once.

The daily chart I was instructed to keep over the two weeks recorded various things; among them Hunger/Urge to Eat. On a scale of one to ten, my urges hovered around two to three. The closest I came to feeling the need to eat was during the second week, during a massage with some citrus-smelling oils, when I thought dreamily, 'I suppose sometimes people eat food. I could eat food. I *used* to eat food; in fact, I distinctly remember doing it. If I *were* to eat food, I would eat some melted cheese.' But even then, I was still not actually hungry. It was remarkable, it was amazing; it was, to be precise, extremely liberating. I felt like I was outside of time, in some weird way, as a result. Days are so demarcated by the rhythm of meals that without them, you start to feel somehow different: unflinching, confident, supra-human. Free. It's hard to put into words. I started to wonder where one signed up for Doris' cult.

*

The miracle burst of energy did not come, however. Not for me, though I could see other people bouncing about and saying how great they felt, and should anyone think that what most people do when they starve themselves is lie on a couch, by turns moaning and hallucinating; far from it. There were four guided walks of differing lengths per day, for those that wanted them, and they were well subscribed to. There was the gym, the yoga studio, the swimming pool – all well attended, the last, even by me, because a little gentle floating about, with no weight on my legs, was okay for ten minutes or so. But no miracle cure arrived, and if I had had any small hope that it would, as the days wore on into the second week, that hope was dashed. And it's the hope, as anyone who has chronic illness will tell you, that kills you. Hope that is every bit as cruel and unforgiving as the unknown illness itself. Hope that leads you on like a false lover, and whose abandonment of you is all the more devastating.

I was not happy. I did not have energy, but one thing I did have, was time. Lots of it. Time, time, time…

Hours stretched away ahead of me; the clinic was also very keen that guests should take the chance for a digital de-tox too, which, apart from streaming one football match, I did.

So I did the best thing anyone can do with lots of time; I read, and that was wonderful. I read more than I had read in years. I'd brought a lot of books with me; finding it just too much of a cliché to take *The Magic Mountain* with me, I'd chosen Mann's first, great, breakthrough novel, for which he won the Nobel Prize: *Buddenbrooks*. If it wasn't quite *The Magic Mountain*, that was okay; I loved it too. When that was done, I read a bunch of other novels; I read some popular science books, some to do with my health (potentially), others to do with ideas for future novels, I hoped.

I lay in the sauna every afternoon, nodding at the other users with small but friendly smiles. I took a class in art in which I drew and painted something I had dreamt the night before: a human heart, out of body and up close in my vision, still beating, dripping a viscous red. I spent a lot of time thinking about how much I liked Germany, and wondering why I didn't come here more often. I went for my daily weigh-in and general check-up with

Suzanna, during which it was unsurprising to see that I was losing a little weight every day.*

I had small chats with other guests: a young American woman suffering badly from arthritis, hoping for the cure that the founder of the clinic had experienced; an easier, more genial chat with the trio of French businessmen; an older American gentleman named Gerry, who was to become a friend – he'd waylaid me in reception one day when he saw me carrying *The New York Times*. I had other treatments: therapeutic massages; the colonic cleanses Doris had promised me were the highlight of the trip (they weren't, but they weren't awful either); sessions with a nutritionist; a psychologist (who was good enough to declare the idea of something being 'all in your head' nonsensical, and that one really had to consider the interaction of mind and body, that it is really hard to even say when ones ends and the other begins); and of course, I had my most important appointments of all, with Herr Dr Wittrock.

I liked him a lot. He was a young man, younger than me at least, who, like Dr G I'd seen in the UK all those years before, had left the orthodox medical system behind in order to blend the best of that science with other, less heard-of approaches. This was becoming something I came across more than once, but I was happy to see there was no question of declaring my name was Mary this time. Everything with Dr W was scientific, whether it be well, or less, known.

And he certainly was precise. He took blood, a lot of it, had it analysed either in the clinic, in the local hospital, or in the case of a test for Lyme disease (which exists in Germany in chronic form

---

* My chart, studiously recorded by the nurses each morning, shows my weight dropping modestly. I begin the two weeks at 84.7kg, 14 days later I become 79.4kg, about a third of a kilo lost each day on average.

even if it doesn't in France), had it sent to Berlin for immediate analysis; and then we discussed everything.

He pointed at this number; he discussed that level. He pondered one or two things, but all in all, he struggled to see why I was so tired, why my legs so weak. But he was not going to give up so easily, and put me on a course of various treatments during my stay, the first of which was intravenous vitamin infusions.

Once again, I felt an amusing connection to the creature in Mary Shelley's novel as I lay on a bed in the medical centre hooked up to a machine. For an hour or so every three days, I watched it draw my blood out into a vessel where it was infused with high levels of Dr W's vitamin mixture, and then transfused back into my bloodstream. Would my 'vital spark' return? I tried to read while the machine hummed and whirred; sometimes I did, sometimes I got frustrated that I couldn't mark-up pages in the book I was reading when I only had one free hand; once, a burst of hypochondria kicked in as I saw an air bubble in one of the tubes. Couldn't that cause a blood clot if it got into my blood vessels? I hesitated for about 30 minutes in a very British way as to whether I was watching my own demise approaching before I finally called a nurse, only for her to dismiss my concerns so lightly I felt as stupid as I probably ought to have felt.

The days ticked by. Just as Mann captures so expertly in *The Magic Mountain*, time did that thing it sometimes does, particularly when we find ourselves in a new environment, or in a period of difference from our usual routine, which is to say it moved both fast and slow at the same time.

I had my treatments and my consultations. I had the best massage I'd ever had. I drank more water than I ever had, and... nothing changed in my body. I could still only stand for a few minutes; I could still only walk for about five or ten minutes in a single go. My mood was awful. My body was refusing to change.

In my mind, though, something was happening. I was becoming more aware of a matter that I had begun to realise was always there, a part of me. In one word, it was this: separateness.

I felt separate from the rest of the world. The sense of being in an unfamiliar location, at the clinic, was shining a spotlight on something I knew I often felt anyway; that I was apart from the world. It's something I felt as a child; I couldn't have told you why, and I still can't, that I felt my family consisted of the other three human beings, and me. Even the family dog felt more like a part of the family – more like my father, mother and brother – than I did. Throughout school, I had never really had many friends; I can literally, as the cliché has it, count on the fingers of one hand the times I invited anyone over to my house throughout 14 years of school. 'My' friends were all friends I borrowed; they were actually my brother's, and I just tagged along. I never joined anything, either metaphorically or literally; I don't do organisations or clubs; I have always simply felt separate from everyone else, and I've never really minded. Sometimes I have had periods of my life where I have thought I ought to mind about this feeling of separateness, and have tried to do something about it, then usually come to the realisation I am fine as I am.

This might be sounding 'poor me' again. If it is, I haven't explained properly. I am not talking about being lonely, or being isolated. I see all the above as just a matter of fact, as a description of how I am. It's not meant to be a cry for sympathy any more than it's meant to be a boast of some weird kind. I just feel separate, and it's fine. It *was* fine.

But. Then.

Then illness came along, and that sense of being apart that Woolf describes in *On Being Ill* so powerfully swept into me, and for the first time in my life, I felt that sense of separateness had been affected, had been *infected*, by the very thing I had never seen it as: isolation. If I had felt separate from the rest of world before, being ill, and thus being unable to participate in the world even as much as I had before, had edged that sense of separation over into one of isolation. I had torn up my passport to the kingdom of the well, or rather, it had been torn up for me by the sickness.

Some of it was down to simple practical matters: I could no longer drift around town at the weekend. If I went out, I needed to make the distance between where I started and where I was going as short and as direct as possible. Doing things like hanging around museums, on your feet for hours, was no longer possible. I could no longer go on walks; I'd sit at home while others might go for a hike into the mountains. During good times, I could manage short excursions; ending up exhausted anyway, and sometimes it was worth it. But overall, the illness was pushing me away from doing things; mostly the sense of extreme fatigue that would follow any overexertion was just *not* worth it.

There were tiresome evenings with friends; people who knew I was ill. After asking how I was, the conversation for the rest of the evening would be about the walks they'd taken; the cycle rides they were going to make; the skiing they'd been doing. And I was sulking then. I didn't say anything, because what could be said? I didn't wish them ill, or for them to not be able to do all the wonderful physical things they could do. I just marvelled at how insensitive people can be. But, as before, maybe that's simply because I am too sensitive.

So I went out less; I accepted fewer offers to speak, trying to manage very carefully the engagements I did accept, and I felt that I was drifting to somewhere no one could follow. Once or twice people may have said to me, and I may have said to myself, that I could join a group of fellow CFS sufferers. That it might be a way of feeling less isolated, or more understood. But I didn't. I do not join things. I don't like groups, and I was fed up enough of listening to myself moan; why would I want to listen to other people moaning too? That was my mindset, no matter how mistaken.

So, I spent my two weeks in the clinic. It was the fall; it was grey, damp, but somehow lovely. My room had a view over rainy Lake Constance; there was still leaf colour around; the gardens were pretty; the buildings, whether old or modern, were elegant. It was peaceful, and I found myself drifting farther and farther away.

*

Halfway during my second week, a small thing occurred. One of the more notable things good Dr Wittrock had found in my blood was that my levels of serotonin were catastrophically low. I could probably have told him that – I knew I was depressed again, and serotonin is a neurotransmitter well-known as vital for the maintenance of good mood. Many modern antidepressants work through action on the levels of serotonin – the class of drug known as SSRIs (selective serotonin reuptake inhibitors) reduce the rate at which the body takes serotonin back out of service, limiting its reabsorption from the bloodstream, though it's unknown exactly how this complicated mechanism works. I'd been prescribed SSRIs several times over the years for depression, and had a love/hate relationship with them; doctors seemed to love giving them to me, I hated taking them. I hated taking them because not only would I invariably get a nasty bunch of side-effects, they also sent my mood all over the place, on one occasion pushing me to the closest I have ever felt to the otherwise indescribable feeling that you have, quite simply, lost your mind. I'd seen two friends kill themselves during the initial 'adjustment period' to anti-depressants, and so vowed that I wouldn't take them anymore. That no matter how depressed or crazy I felt, that it would be down to my own body's biochemistry, and not the little-understood biochemistry that a doctor wanted me to introduce into my system.

Because, once again, it seemed I was more sensitive than most. I knew several friends who were taking SSRIs without problems, or even the mildest side-effects, while for me they were a minefield. Instead, many years previously, I'd tried a 'natural' alternative. 5-HTP, or 5-hydroxytryptophan, is a naturally occurring amino acid and is a precursor in the production of serotonin. It's available off the shelf as a supplement; many people successfully use it to boost their mood, but when I took it, I found it made me thirsty. Massively thirsty, constantly; so thirsty I had continual headaches, and after persisting for a week or two, had given it up.

5-HTP was what Dr Wittrock suggested to me now. He was mindful of my experience with anti-depressants, and so proposed this more natural approach. I told him about my previous experience with it; he assured me that thirst was not a known side-effect. I didn't argue, and I took it, as he prescribed; one pill that morning, a second before bed, and sure enough, back came the raging thirst, the headaches. I lay awake all night with my heart pounding for no reason, and the next day, drank litre after litre of water. I went to ask Dr W about it, and he was surprised, telling me he'd never come across this reaction before.

Still, there has to be a first time for everything. There has to be someone who is the first to get something, to feel something; there have to be people who lie at the edges of whatever bell curve you happen to be considering. It doesn't make you special; in fact, as I was feeling, it makes you a pain in the arse. It meant doctors gave you things that they gave other people with no troubles at all, and then conclude that you must be making it up or generally being psychosomatic/hypochondriac in some way. It means you're allergic to something that it seems no one else is; it means you have to be that 'nervy one'; that awkward person who asks if there's any gluten-free bread or lactose-free alternatives around.

And all of these things make you feel a little more separate, just as Woolf had written; you go alone into illness, no matter what happens to you, the exact same thing has not happened to anyone else. You go alone. You cannot tell anyone else how you feel, not really. They can listen, and they can give you their sympathy, and it can be welcome; but no one else can be in your body. You go alone.

Now that's one view, but I am not sure I believe it, even if I sometimes feel it. We humans are allowed to be contradictory, aren't we? So to everyone who says, "you can't know how I feel", I'm tempted to offer this thought by way of discussion: No, I haven't had your exact experience. No one has, of course. We each have our own, unique life. But there are only so many emotions in the world: happiness, excitement, fear, doubt and so on. So when you have suffered pain, know that so has everyone else. And everyone else has suffered fear, and worry. Not for the same reason, it's true. But the result is the same, and so, I *do* know how you feel. You have felt fear, and so have I, and I empathise with you for that, even if I can't empathise with the reason why.

But at the time, I was feeling sorry for myself, and it was because of this overwhelming sense of desperate isolation. That need to understand, to connect, truly, with other people, the rest of the world, had never seemed to be that pressing to me; but now I was frantic for it, it seemed as far away as ever. I had barely begun to get used to not getting used to it: to not knowing what the hell was going on.

Yet even then, I could sense, underneath my sulking self, that there was a bigger truth here: I might have had no idea what was happening to me, but neither does anyone else. Not really. We may think we are in control of our lives, but the person who truly believes that is surely and simply waiting for it to be disproved.

They are simply waiting for the 'until it happens to you' moment to arrive in their life. It only takes the appearance of a thing like an unknown illness to make that painfully clear.

Writers, non-writers; the healthy and the sick; we are all living in undiagnosis. But that's something, at least, something worth remembering; we are all together in being alone.

*

I finished my time at the clinic. On the anti-penultimate day, I was allowed one whole apple. To be eaten 'very slowly'. It looked so incredible, like a beautiful art object, a small miracle of nature, never before seen by a mortal. I took a photo of it. I'd been sternly warned that stopping eating is much easier than starting to eat again – you have to take it very carefully. On the penultimate day, I was allowed three small meals of rice, one with chicken, and with the addition of a small piece of fruit for dessert. And then it was the final day and time to go. It was a shame to leave, but the total on the bill (that, having seen, I was suddenly extremely glad I wasn't paying) reminded me why most of us don't spend two or three weeks in beautifully-situated clinics in the mountains or on lakesides, while a team of expert professional medical staff cater to every twitch of the scales, every shiver in the blood. And I was glad to be going home; for I had learned a thing or two, after all.

For one, not eating for the best part of two weeks goes a fair way to helping you address your relationship with food. Whether it's a good one or a bad one, taking food out of life for a time means you come back to it with interest; perhaps even with insight: how can you truly see something you never stand back from?

A big message that the clinic wanted everyone to go away with was this; eat more slowly. Chew your food properly; chew it slowly, chew it for a long time. Do not rush while you eat; savour it. Eating quickly, even if you're not stressed, fools the body into thinking you *are* stressed – that you are preparing for difficult times – and what that means is that the body actually processes things differently; for example, fat is more likely to be stored, in preparation for times of possible hunger ahead.

As someone who has never had a great interest in food – largely because of that thing of what a damn lot of time it wastes – this was good to be told.

I was looking forward to going home, and eating normally, with that newfound respect for food, something that has lasted to some great degree. I was looking forward to re-toxifying myself with wine. And also, I was looking forward to following up a lead I had found while at the clinic. Not from anything they had given me, but from a book I had read while there; an extraordinarily interesting book in its own right, though it wasn't the subject of the book that interested me the most, but the story of its author; for it seemed she was someone who had gone through almost exactly what I had when I became sick, two years before, in Malaysia. Here was something that made me feel less separate; something that made me think I might be less alone in the mysterious journey I'd been on than I thought. So I wrote to her.

11 – Gut Feelings

'Please drop your trousers,' said Dr Tench.

I blinked.

'Listen,' he said, 'The best thing I can suggest is a massive injection of steroids. It'll tell us something. Drop your trousers.'

It hurt to sit for a day or so after my visit to see Dr Tench, a London specialist in autoimmune conditions. He was a friendly, professional 'chap' of a particularly English athletic manner; despite the smart suit, he looked as though he was just back from whupping someone at squash in a private sports club in Mayfair. I'd got in touch with him as a result of reading an extremely fascinating book about bacteria. Yes, there are such things, and this one was written by Alanna Collen. It's called *10% Human*, and I can recommend it if you want to freak yourself out a little bit.

What interested me about her book was not only all the remarkable things about bacteria, some of which you want to know and some of which you probably don't, but her own story. Like me, she had fallen ill with some mysterious, undiagnosed illness after a trip to Malaysia. After several years, her search had finally led her to Dr Tench, who had been able to diagnose a rare autoimmune condition brought on by a tick-borne infection. With a vast and lengthy course of antibiotics, she had found a cure, of sorts. Of sorts, because her journey wasn't over yet, as things turned out.

Like the world in the grip of a pandemic, I was hoping for a cure myself – a cure of my own tiny world – and so was once again caught in that weird vice of wanting to find out what was wrong, even if what was wrong was not something you wanted to find out you had. I still felt it would be better knowing than not knowing.

'From what you've told me, it doesn't sound like anything in my field,' Dr Tench said, sympathetically. 'But there's a simple way to find out. We'll give you a huge single dose of steroids. If your symptoms improve at all, that shows it's possibly an autoimmune issue. If not, not. How does that sound?'

In for a penny, in for a pound, and three years into the illness, I had spent a few of those by now. Time to thrash the bank balance once more. That was my attitude, so I duly lowered my trousers and bent over. If I was expecting the usual doctors' reassurance at this point, I was to be surprised.

'This might hurt a bit...'

*

He was right. More importantly, my symptoms did not improve. Well, I told myself, you don't want an autoimmune problem anyway. That can be really nasty. And at least it was one more thing ticked off the list.

I was left, however, with a newfound obsession in bacteria, thanks to Collen's book. I bought a couple more tomes on the subject; on the relatively new field of discovery about our relationship with bacteria, both good and bad. If you're thinking I turned into Howard Hughes at this point, and became an extreme germophobe, that's not the kind of obsession I'm talking about. Despite any possible hypochondriac tendencies, I wasn't at all disturbed to learn from the book that, if you count by number of cells present, your body is just 10% 'you' and 90% bacteria. If you count by the number of genes present in the genome, the figures are even wilder. The human genome has 21,000 genes. That might sound like a lot, but it's barely more than an earthworm; less than a water flea, and roughly half what a rice plant has. And we think we're so damn smart. In fact, Collen explained, if you make an estimate of the total bacterial genome you're playing host to, you get a figure of around 4.4 million genes. Which, by that reckoning, makes you about half a per cent human. It makes you a vehicle for carrying bacteria through space and time, which, from an evolutionary perspective, is just what they're after. There is even a theory that our own mitochondria, our little energy production centres tucked away inside our cells, were once bacteria that hitched a lift by integrating themselves into some other, slightly less primitive early lifeform. Nor was I concerned by facts such as that you have around 900 species of bacteria living in your nostrils alone, or ten million bacteria per millilitre in some parts of your gut.

What I was concerned about was Collen's central thesis, and that of other, similar scientists, about the use of antibiotics – that while they might have made life more tolerable in the short term, they're severely ruining our health in the long term.

In the course of human history, antibiotics are still new. They are a very modern thing. And if you consider a range of various 'modern' ailments, things which were extremely rare in our grandparents' and even parents' generations – things like diabetes, obesity, auto-immune disorders, allergies, MS, irritable bowel; not to mention mental health matters such as autism, depression, ADD, OCD, Tourette's and so on – all these conditions are on the rise, and sharply. If you plot a graph of the rise in the use of antibiotics over the rise of all these conditions, they match, rather disturbingly. Of course, correlation does not prove causation, but Collen is one of the people who are researching this matter.

From *10% Human*, 'Your dentist's autistic son has more company than ever before, as 1 in 68 children (but 1 in every 42 boys) are on the autistic spectrum. Back in the early 1940s, autism was so rare it hadn't even been given a name. Even by the time records began in 2000, it was less than half as common as it is now.'

The theory being proposed in various quarters is that we are ruining the vital relationship we have with a range of beneficial bacterial species in our gut, and the explosion of 'modern' ailments is the result. This was the indeed the conclusion that Alanna Collen had come to in her research, and through her own personal experience; the antibiotic cure for her infection had destroyed her gut's ecosystem, leading to a range of other health problems. Only by correcting that bacterial destruction in her own private ecosystem imbalance and changing her diet was she able to cure herself properly. Over an email exchange, she told me how she had, for a time, a long time, been put in the 'CFS bucket' by the health services and how, once put there, it does you no use in terms of diagnosis or treatment. I knew this now to be true; once you've had that label slapped on you, little or nothing further is done because it is believed that there is little more to do. Not only that, but any other ailment that comes along is often not investigated either, since it's deemed to be just another emanation of your CFS.

This is particularly the case if you're a woman. The modern term MUS, or Medically Unexplained Symptoms, has been replacing that of Conversion Disorder, which in turn grew out of a belief in hysteria, and all of these things are considered to overwhelmingly be female phenomena. As is well-known, the term *hysteria* derives from *uterus*, and doctors from the Greeks onwards have seen such issues as essentially female problems. There's a long history of prejudice here, one which has been doing women harm for centuries; once that 'psych' label is applied, you are unlikely to be offered any interventions in your illness that treat it as something physiological, and not something all in your head. Statistically, therefore, I was a less common case – a man being told my condition was psychosomatic. Rarer, though not that unusual. On average, women take the brunt of these slapdash diagnoses, or lack of diagnoses, I would prefer to say. Yes, it's 'true statistically' that more women are diagnosed with ME/CFS than men,[i] and that more women are diagnosed with psychosomatic conditions, such as MUS, as men. And why might that be? If you're tempted to think that these statistics must prove either that women are really more likely to suffer such problems, or that it must show that ME/CFS and similar illnesses really are 'all in your head', then you might like to consider an alternative possibility, one which is terrifying, denigrating to women, undoubtedly harmful to us all, and completely unethical. It's something, which if the general public were aware of it, would cause riots in the streets. Or ought to.

It's this. Diane O'Leary, the bioethicist, explained to me how modern psych textbooks *literally instruct* doctors to diagnose ten times as many women with psychosomatic disorders as men.[ii] A result of the unchanging prejudice that underlies the changing names of 'hysterical' conditions, doctors are quite simply instructed to aim to diagnose more women than men with psychosomatic issues. No wonder then, that the best official statistics we have show more women are diagnosed with ME/CFS than men; your doctor is literally told to make it that way.*

On the face of this, if you're a woman who gets a case of ME/CFS, or fibromyalgia, or similar; you're much more likely to have to fight having the 'pysch' label being applied to you. And when it is, 'physical' treatments will stop. This obviously harms women. It also, in a different way, harms men; perpetuating the stereotype that men don't fall prey to mental health problems so much as women, which in turn prevents many men from seeking help for depression; probably the reason why the highest cause of death among men under fifty in the UK is suicide. It also

---

* If you're as horrified by this as I was, you might want to read the best book on the subject I know of: *Doing Harm: The Truth About How Bad Medicine* and *Lazy Science Leave Women Dismissed, Misdiagnosed, and Sick*, by Maya Dusenbery.

reinforces those prejudices about the 'type of person' who gets ME/CFS. Had Dr T, all those years before, just glanced down my medical records, seen 'depression' under my case notes and 'writer' under my profession, and made a snap, bigoted assumption? Writers are crazy, right? Diane O'Leary and I wondered what would have happened if I had walked into her office with short hair, a polo shirt, and a CV that told her I was something 'normal' – an accountant, a banker, whatever. Just not, for God's sake, a *writer*.

In the face of the pandemic, this is a story which will multiply… five-fold, ten-fold, more? Who knows? But it's a story the general public needs to be made aware of, because whether or not Long Covid is the same thing as ME/CFS, or a trigger for ME/CFS, or another misunderstood chronic illness entirely, there is going to be an avalanche of stories like the one that happened to me and other sufferers of Undiagnosis.

And if this happens to you, if you become 'undiagnosed', these are the dangers that beset you. As a retired NHS GP explained to me, if you go to your doctor and they cannot determine what is wrong with you, they nevertheless have to tick a box at the end of your consultation to 'code' your illness for medical records. In your case, therefore, they may well tick a box marked MUS. If you were to learn that this means Medically Unexplained Symptoms, you might not even make much of the fact, not realising that you have technically just been diagnosed with a psychosomatic ailment, a mental health disorder. A glimpse at the powerful, hidden reasons behind this choice of diagnosis is to be found in the appendix to this book.

Utterly unaware of all of this when I first became ill, I learned it all the hard way, and in retrospect may have tried to handle some things differently. I would certainly have been more persistent in fighting the label that gave me a psychosomatic condition.

And it can be worth doing that; Alanna Collen's case was one that showed that sometimes persistence, and your own research, can pay off; she had finally found what her problem was – Undifferentiated Connective Tissue Disease – and with Dr Tench's help had been able to manage it. She is now well. How many people, like myself, remain ill, having been told the problem is all in our heads, when perhaps we just needed a stroke of luck in the diagnostic department, is unknown. The answer is probably terrifying.

*

Meanwhile, I stayed ill, and I kept reading about bacteria, and the gut. The relationship between those two things, and our health, seemed indisputable. Not just our physical health, but our mental health too. Here's just one fact to prove that point; it's now known that 90% of the serotonin we produce, the serotonin so vital for good mood, is produced in our gut. The gut itself has been desperately neglected by medicine. As one doctor I spoke to explained; 'when I went to medical school, we perhaps had one half-day looking at the gut. It was perceived to be a rather boring tube through which the waste products of digestion pass.'

Yet it's now starting to be perceived very differently; as the fundament on which our health, or lack of it, rests. To give another somewhat mind-altering statistic, the gut has 100 million neurons; more than the spinal cord or the peripheral nervous system. Some researchers have taken to calling the enteric nervous system, as it's properly known, the 'second brain', because of its importance to the body. While this second brain does not engage in conscious or higher thought processes, it is responsible for controlling digestion, mediating the immune response, and very probably affects our emotional state to a large degree. It's been found that 90% of the messages travelling along the vagus nerve, which is the major nerve pathway between the brain and the gut, are travelling 'upwards' from the gut to the brain, not the other way around. Your gut is doing a lot of thinking for you, albeit largely unobserved. It's obvious to someone who believes in the history of words and expressions that the phrase 'gut feeling' probably meant something all along; we all feel butterflies in the stomach at times; we have a 'gut instinct' about matters that sometimes the head-mind is conflicted over. We now begin to know why we say these things.

*

It's not just the relationship between the gut and the brain that we are having to reassess – another book on the subject by Emeran Mayer called *The Mind-Gut Connection* explained that it's better to think of these systems as a three-way conversation, between the brain, the gut, and *the bacteria in our gut*.

I also started to read about other little discussed matters, such as the use of various chemicals that are also destroying our gut's health. I read about triclosan, for example. If you've never heard of it, your gut has; you've almost certainly ingested some, especially if you live in the USA. This is one of those anti-bacterial chemicals added to a range of products; things like soap, detergents, washing-up liquid, toothpaste, mouthwashes, toys, chopping boards, and so on. All those lovely adverts promising spotless surfaces in your home, those adverts which love to plant the seed of fear that a home is dangerous (especially to your babies!! Make sure you are worried about your babies!!) unless 100% microbe-free. The problem with triclosan is, despite its widespread use, it has never been shown to be safe for human consumption. In the USA, only chemicals that are directly added to food have to be shown to be safe. Anything that goes on our food *before* it's harvested, or anything that comes in contact with us through non-food means, is just fine. Despite the fact that it goes in your mouth, and that most people swallow a little of it every time you brush, toothpaste does not count as food; and triclosan is present in a great number of household name brands. There is an increasing amount of evidence that triclosan and other similar chemical products are bad for us; destroying good bacteria, as well as the incredibly important but little understood lining of the gut, a lining which has to do the amazing job of letting good things through into the bloodstream (i.e., the useful products of digestion), while keeping bad things out, things like bad bacteria, viruses, food waste products, and so on. The amount of evidence mounting against triclosan was enough that in 2017 the FDA banned its use in a range of antiseptic washes, where it had also not been shown to be any more effective than normal soap and water. But it's still fine in toothpaste, apparently. And this is just one chemical of hundreds in everyday use with similarly unknown toxicities.

*

It was all very fascinating stuff. Somewhat alarming. There was just one problem; it wasn't making me any better.

I'd been giving my gut some thought. There are some schools of thought that forms of CFS might be due to yet another disputed thing called Leaky-Gut syndrome, according to which your precious gut lining is allowing some of those bad things through, as well as the good. Thus, you are being gently poisoned; the toxins in the blood and other bodily tissues resulting in the fatigue, muscle pain, aching joints etc. There's even now a test for how permeable your gut lining is, and I realised – as I read about this stuff – that I'd already had it. It was one of the more obscure tests that the good Herr Dr Wittrock had put into motion during my time playing Hans Castorp on the shores of Lake Constance. The action for this test revolves around a measure of a thing called zonulin; which, I thought to myself, is proof once again that scientists make up the names of substances in general and medicines in particular by sitting around a Czech Scrabble board late at night with a book of Greek mythology in one hand and a bag of crystal meth in the other.

As it turns out, zonulin is not Flash Gordon's arch-enemy, but rather, a protein that controls the permeability of your gut lining; it's thought to be part of the story in coeliac disease. I'd had mine measured, and the results showed nothing too serious – I was near the upper limit of gut permeability, but still within the normal range. Nevertheless, it was worth thinking about and – taking the advice of Alanna Collen and others – I started taking pro- and pre-biotics, and eating even more vegetables and avoiding all processed food where possible. At home, I mostly ate well anyway, but started switching over completely to organic vegetables and chicken. All in all, I couldn't think how I could be much nicer to my gut, and yet, after many, many months of this, I was still ill. Just the same; not the tiniest bit better at all. It can't hurt to improve your diet; to improve the bacterial balance in your gut. It can't hurt to stop eating vegetables and wheat products that have had glyphosate sprayed on them, for example, which then enters your body. (If you don't know what glyphosate is, and what it's doing to human health, I'm guessing it won't be long before you hear about it.) So I didn't regret any of this effort, but, yet again, I was left in the dark, not knowing.

*

All this thinking about the gut, and the fact that we sometimes neglect our gut feelings at our peril, had left me wondering whether I ought to stop finding answers in my head.

Before moving to France, I'd been seeing an amazing osteopath in Cambridge. Helen was a Russian doctor, but since her medical qualifications were Russian, she was unable to practise medicine in the UK. Instead, she was working as an osteopath, and had worked wonders for a neighbour of mine. I saw Helen over the course of a few months, and while she wasn't able to help with my illness, she was remarkable in other ways. Once, as she walked around me in small circles, prodding bits and pieces and muttering to herself, she described an accident I'd had.

'You fell. Like this, so. You landed on your elbow and jammed your shoulder joint up, like this. So.'

I listened to her, mystified. Then I remembered a skiing accident I'd had ages ago, a year or two before I became ill – Helen had been able to see this from the traces left behind in my ribs; after *four whole years*. There were other things of this nature that left me convinced that, were this the middle ages, she would either have been venerated or burnt at the stake.

One day, she said to me, 'Marcus, where do you write from?'

'Oh,' I said, 'well, I'm really lucky, I have this lovely little shed in the –'

'No, no. No. I mean, where do you write *from*?'

She looked at me and this time I understood.

I didn't hesitate.

'From here,' I said, and pointed at my head.

'Yes,' she said. 'I thought so.'

She gave me one of her hard Russian stares.

'Maybe it's time to try writing from somewhere else.'

*

I drove home, with one of those unexpected moments that occur in a life, sometimes where you suddenly are given a different view of the whole thing. I almost wept at the thought: I have been in my head, I thought. For so long. For *so* long. "All In My Head", I thought, and the association was not lost on me. And now I could see how this illness, and the worry about it, was pushing me even further into my head. Not just because I could no longer do much with my body; but in some other way, I had become so wrapped up in the intellectual pursuit of health. Just as I had been wrapped up in the intellectual pursuit of novels, for over twenty years.

Was there, I wondered, a way to write from the gut instead? Could you write from other places? From the heart? From the legs, even? And if you could, would you find a balance?

I didn't know what any of this meant, and perhaps it's just a mental game, but I determined to try to write more with other body parts from then on, even if just a little; it had to be good.

And I also decided it was maybe time to let my gut try to decide what was wrong with me. Did my gut know whether this illness that had crept into me one day was all in my head? Or all in my body? Or a bit of both? What did my gut feelings have to say about all this?

I listened. I tried to watch, without much judgement or critical intervention, what my gut feeling was about being sick, and I got answers. And that was the problem; I got answers in the plural. One day, it seemed to say, yes, Marcus, this is all in your head. And the next it would say, don't be stupid, you don't want to be ill, neither does your body, and the answer is clearly that you were made sick from some infection in Asia, which either has not left, or which has, but which has corrupted your bodily functions nonetheless. It seemed I didn't have a gut feeling, I had gut *feelings*; and the damn things just couldn't make up their minds.

*

Then, another small moment of coincidence came along.

It was somewhere between late 2016, early 2017. I had been reading about all this stuff – bacteria, antibiotics, gut linings, the chemical destruction of both the global and the individual ecosystems – and hoping to find a solution to my illness, a way to cure me from the inside out, through diet, when by chance I came across something else.

I was writing again, but I was still determined that I would never write about being ill, in any shape or form. Yet as I look back, I can see that that resolve must have already been weakening, because I had decided that if (just theoretically, of course) I *did* write about being ill, I wouldn't write about CFS, but that I would make up a chronic but disputed illness. Just to distance things a little from myself. So as not to be so self-indulgent. (You might laugh at this point and if you do, I don't blame you.) If I did make up an illness, I thought, I'd call it MCS, a private, self-indulgent joke, since those are my initials. It sounds like something pretty ghastly anyway. Fairly terminal. 'Have you heard? She's got MCS. Oh, it's just awful.'

Then, as I was writing a monograph about snow, I came across the fact that there is a real (though disputed) illness called MCS. It stands for Multiple Chemical Sensitivity, and the best-known community of sufferers is in the improbably named town of Snowflake, Arizona.

I read about MCS. It sounded truly awful. I read interviews with sufferers, I read books, and the more I read, the more I wondered if it was something like MCS that had been happening to me. (It was my name, after all. Stranger things have happened.)

So one fine spring day in 2017, having dragged my way through a book tour around the US, I tacked on a few days at the end and made a trip to the desert to see the people who call themselves The Canaries. And if I thought my time with bacteria was over, I was mistaken; because Life was about to play one of its better cosmic jokes on me.

----

[i] https://me-pedia.org/wiki/Sex_differences_in_myalgic_
encephalomyelitis_and_chronic_fatigue_syndrome
[ii] Entry on somatic symptom disorder, American Family Physician, by Kurlansik and Maffei (2016): "Females tend to present with somatic

symptom disorder more often than males, with an estimated female-to-male ratio of 10:1."

12 – Snowflakes in the Desert

'Have you come to write about us?' asked Susie, a little suspiciously. If she was suspicious, she had good reason to be. She, like all the other sufferers of MCS, both in Snowflake, and elsewhere, have had enough of being doubted. Or disbelieved, or even just plain laughed at. And all these things are common.

'The crazies in the desert; that's how people like to see us,' she explained as she drove me from the airport. 'Gullible little snowflakes.'

'No,' I said, 'I haven't come to write about you. I just want to see if you can help me understand what's going on.'

That was true. I was still absolutely determined not to write about illness. Similarly, I'd always had a thing about writers writing novels about writers; a lot of writers do it, and it always seemed so self-indulgent to me. "Write what you know", they say. It's one of the aphorisms about writing I can't stand. You should write what you don't know; that's (mostly) my view. Write what you want to explore, what you want to find out, what you want to stumble across. Why would I want to write something I already know any more than anyone would want to read something they already know? It can work sometimes, yes, if either of the parties are after a sense of familiarity, or to act as witness. But mostly, as I writer, I have just been trying to go to places that are new for me. So I had always put off writing about a writer – for years – until I'd finally given in, and done it. Now I was determined not to write about being ill – it seemed even more personally self-indulgent than writing about a writer.

'No,' I assured Susie, 'I just figured you guys might have some answers for me.'

Susie was the unofficial spokesperson for the group; she handled a lot of media enquiries, and the tricky thing for her was knowing which ones were going to help, and which ones weren't. It wasn't just a question of shutting up shop and saying no to everyone, because she knows that if they are ever going to get their illness taken seriously, they need publicity. They just need the kind that knows that there is something genuinely wrong with them, and not the kind that just points and laughs at the 'crazies in the desert.'

She told me about some of the people who'd come in the past: TV crews, journalists. A British novelist who'd come with a photographer, who'd seemed to understand but had then written a somewhat sneery piece for *The Guardian*. I could see these things had hurt Susie, personally, and I didn't want to hurt her.

'We'll take you around, have you meet with a few folks. You might wanna talk to Harry; he's got problems with his legs, like you. Chronic Lyme and Bartonella, that's his trouble.'

I liked her immediately. She was tiny, smart, and funny. She had a brightness in her eyes, but one which every so often would be replaced by a look of something else, fear, pain, a memory... I wasn't sure which. Then it would vanish and she'd laugh at something, often something about which it seemed strange to laugh.

The day before, I'd taken a flight from LA to Phoenix, and stopped the night there near the airport, in the kind of featureless big chain hotel that America does really well. Endless corridors; vast amounts of brown. I did something I rarely do and ate steak in the restaurant. While I did, I looked at the heat outside, which was visible. At nine the next morning, back at the airport, the temperature was pushing 110F. It was the first of May.

I made my way through security to my gate; a huge field of stained carpet, hardly anyone around, the only thing in sight outside a small private jet.

The private jet turned out to be my plane: 'Boutique Air' was a small operation. I liked to think their fleet had been commandeered from a corrupt billionaire who'd met his just desserts. In-air catering was a bottle of water you helped yourself to from a cool-box in the aisle; there wasn't room or height for anyone to come down it while in the air. Surprisingly, the plane was nearly full; the other six passengers seemed to be a group of orthodontists heading for Show Low, another improbably named town, so-called because it had been won over an interminable game of poker, finally settled by whoever drew the lowest card.

From Show Low to Snowflake, named after the two Mormons who founded it – Mr Snow and Mr Flake – was a ride of about half an hour, during which time I got to know Susie a little bit. She told me about how the MCS came on, and what it had meant for her; the struggles with doctors, with insurance companies, and so on. She'd been in a wheelchair when she'd first moved out to the desert; now, she wasn't too bad if she kept away from the kinds of chemicals that set off a reaction in her.

'People are so dumb,' she said. 'They look at you and think you look okay, so there must be nothing wrong with you.'

I agreed with her; I'd already had my crash course in that.

'And then, if you are only okay if you keep away from the world, they also think there's nothing wrong with you. But that's the point; we had to come away. We had to get away from the world, or else we'll get sick again.'

It's for this reason they call themselves The Canaries; just as in coalmines of old, the canary sensed deadly toxic mine gas before it could kill a miner. These 'Sensitives', to give them another of their names, believe that they are the thin end of the wedge; they are the people more prone to being affected by all the chemicals we're breathing, bathing in, eating and drinking; they are the early warning sign of what's coming to all of us unless we wise up about stuff. Stuff like triclosan and glyphosate and chlorpyrifos.

I'd written to the community website; Susie had written back and invited me to stay with her for a few nights so I could learn about MCS, and more generally, EI – environmental illness. She'd laid out certain directions for me, if I wanted to come, mostly around washing. I'd followed these instructions meticulously; I'd brought with me a set of old clothes, which I had washed three times in bicarbonate of soda before I left, and sealed in a plastic bag until the morning I left for Show Low. For three days, I had stopped using shampoo or body wash, and had showered and washed my hair every day with bicarb and nothing else. On the book tour, I'd flown on average once every day. Aside from the exhaustion, even using mobility assistance to get through the airports, and to and from taxis, I'd had the small bother of having my suitcase turned over by TSA every single time. It took me a few days to realise what the large plastic bag of bi-carbonate of soda probably looked like to X-ray scanners.

Despite my precautions, Susie wasn't happy. I was still giving something off, so we rode with the windows down in her car, and when I got to her house, she dug out a box of old clothes that she keeps for visitors.

'Choose what fits; they're all clean.'

By clean, she didn't just mean clean. She also meant 'off-gassed' – a process of leaving clothes, or anything else that might contain harmful chemicals, to air, outside, for a long time until they're safe to wear without causing someone with MCS any trouble. It's this kind of practice that the doubters of MCS doubt. I looked at it all with an open mind; I was in no place to judge anyone who'd been told their illness was 'all in their head'.

*

Susie's friend Deb came over; she was friendly too, though she kept her distance from me. She was even more sensitive than

Susie, and whatever I was giving off was giving her a headache. In the end, we sat outside on Susie's porch, and we talked not only about being ill, but about being ill when hardly anyone else believes you're ill.

It wasn't just the doctors; it wasn't just the insurance companies. It was friends, it was family. It was husbands and wives. It was children. Deb told me how she hadn't seen her daughter in well over a decade; and almost everyone Susie took me to meet had a similar tale.

'The worst thing?' said Deb. 'The worst thing was when my own daughter looked at me and said, "there's nothing wrong with you".'

*

If Snowflake left me with one profound impression, it was this: everyone was single. Everyone was on their own; with just one exception – an older couple who I didn't meet. They were the exception probably because they both had MCS. Maybe they were together because of MCS, not despite it; I didn't find out. For everyone else, the stories were all the same; the end of each one, divorce.

It was heart-breaking; proof, should anyone need it, that not only is it hard to be ill, it's hard to live for, or care for, someone being ill. If the sufferers of certain conditions get little attention, the people who love them get even less. The strain, no matter how much you love someone, no matter how much you try to rationalise everything, can simply be too much, and frequently is.

I felt a terribly long way from home, out there in the Navajo Desert. I listened to story after story, of all the people I met in Snowflake, and it was thoroughly depressing. Yet, though there was a degree of bitterness present, which I found more than understandable, for the most part, all the Canaries I spoke to were funny, warm people. They all seemed calm; they all seemed, when

I thought about it, to have accepted what had happened to them, and with grace. I felt very far from that graceful acceptance; I was desperate for answers, and so I asked all sorts of people all sorts of questions. I spoke to Harry about his legs and his Bartonella and Lyme; he told me how he'd diagnosed himself with his own microscope and his own blood. But now, he'd found a doctor who was starting him on a massive course of antibiotics, and that would lick it. I told him I hoped it would, and didn't mention good bacteria.

*

'You know, no one wants to live in the desert,' Susie said one evening. 'Who wants to live out here? No one sane. But we're the lucky ones; we're the few who actually managed to get our insurance companies to believe we're sick, and pay out. And even then, it was a fight.'

And the unlucky ones, I asked?

Susie gave a sad shrug. No doubt the homeless population of America contains an awful lot of sick people who couldn't convince their insurance company to pay out, and who lost everything: job, home, marriage. Life itself.

I chatted with a lovely man named Scott. Again, I'd liked him immediately; I could tell I was going to like him before we even spoke, as he walked over to meet Susie and me, sitting on someone else's porch. He was a few years younger than me; he was calm, intelligent. Open. I was keen to talk to him because here was someone I felt was well placed to answer the burning question of whether these mysterious illnesses are all in the head, because he told me he'd studied Psychology before he got sick. Since then, he'd spent around a decade sleeping rough, camping on people's porches, and so on, unable to tolerate the chemicals present in most modern homes. Like all the other Canaries, he'd come to Snowflake to escape the toxicity of the rest of the world; not only is Snowflake remote, and thus away from sources of pollution, it's also very high, at nearly six thousand feet up – the air is dry and clean. It's for the same reason that TB patients were sent to the region a hundred years ago and more. The high deserts of Arizona, New Mexico, and California served as respite for the tubercular in America, just as the Swiss Alps did for Europeans.

I was feeling sensitive about asking Scott my question, but I had to. I was nervous he'd think I was doubting him, but he was a scientist; I hoped he'd understand.

'You must have wondered,' I ventured. 'At some point, it must have crossed your mind to wonder whether they're right. Those doctors, the ones who say it's all in your head?'

'Yes, it crossed my mind,' he said. He didn't mind the question at all, and I was relieved. 'It crossed my mind, but it's just not true. I wish it were, because if it were all in my mind, I might be able to do something about it.'

*

Over the course of the next couple of days, I met half a dozen or so sufferers of MCS. I saw a few more than I met; in the distance one day, I saw the sole couple in the community walking up the red sand track to their house, the husband supporting his wife, though I could only tell she was a woman because Susie told me. She was hidden in a white suit, like a hazmat suit; complete with a hood, a mask, dark glasses.

'She's got it real bad,' Susie said. 'Everything gets to her.'

We watched them making their painfully slow way towards their house for a moment longer, then we drove on. We were heading further out into the desert to meet another of the community, a Dane who'd been living and working in the States for years. He'd been really bad with MCS, been through what everyone else had to fight to get people to believe there's actually something wrong with him, that he wasn't just faking it.

He, too, was super-friendly. He had a big infectious grin and a warm and open manner, just like everyone else I'd met. He was proud of his home; he'd managed to get somewhere safe for him to live, and stay as well as he could.

'But if I spend a day back in the normal world, I get sick real fast,' he explained. Like Susie, and many of the others, they would wear masks on trips to town if they were going to be exposed to too much that might cause them problems. Like many EI sufferers, this great Dane also had trouble with electricity, but he showed me how he'd converted his home to run on a system that made it safer for him; how he'd stripped out most of the electrics in his car, to also make it less damaging for him to use. He could do all this because he'd been an engineer.

'Hey,' he said, just as I was leaving. 'You're a writer? Maybe you should write a book about us!'

I shook my head.

'Oh, no,' I said. 'That's not why I've come. Anyway, I doubt anyone would want to read a book about a bunch of sick people in the desert.'

He laughed.

'Well, it's an idea.'

*

Whatever else these sick people in the desert are, I decided, they're not gullible. They're not stupid. I met engineers, a psychologist, an academic. They were mostly highly-educated and/or intelligent people. And they surely weren't faking it. Could you sleep on other people's porches for ten years, just to fake something? I know I couldn't, and I had by now had first-hand experience of that: what Susie and I hadn't cleared up before I arrived was where I was going to sleep. Her home was not large; a single living room/kitchen with her bed in one corner, a bathroom and a utility room. There was no room for guests. I'd suggested camping; she knew from experience that the tents I might rent from any local suppliers would be coated in chemicals; not good at all to bring into their community.

The solution, as it turned out, was that I was going to sleep on her porch, on an old camp bed. The first evening, she fetched me a stack of blankets and a sleeping bag; some cushions, and we made up a bed. In two directions, there were walls; the cinder block wall of the outside of her house, with a corner made by the portion of her 'bedroom' which jutted out, and a large sliding glass door. In the other two, there was desert, the red sand of Navajo County stretching off into the distance, dotted here and there with creosote or juniper bushes.

At dusk, we all decided we were tired. Deb went off to sleep in the back of her pick-up truck, as she'd been doing for over fifteen years. Susie pottered around inside, while I decided how to make the most of my sleeping arrangements. Not getting undressed was my first thought; it might have been Arizona, but it was only the first of May, and we were at way over five thousand feet. It was cold. Just as I started to settle down, Susie poked her head around the glass door.

'Hey, you might wanna check inside your boots every time you put them on again. In case of rattlers. Or scorpions.'

Then she noticed something, and came outside to close the gate between the bit of the desert that she called the 'yard' and the bit of desert that was the rest of Arizona.

'We'll just shut you in,' she said, as she made her way back into the house. 'We wouldn't want a coyote to sneak in here and, you know, eat your face off.'

And she laughed, with her sometimes inappropriate, but never unkind, laugh.

*

It was indeed cold. In the morning, I woke with the sun, around five, and watched it burn the frost away. The desert steamed for a half hour or so. I lay, shivering a little. I hadn't slept well, but it had been spectacular; the clear high Arizona night sky full of stars, the Milky Way as strong as I had ever seen it. As the sun lifted, I heard a buzzing just above my head; tiny blue hummingbirds come to feed at the sugar drip Susie had left there for them. Beautiful, it had been, memorable too. And distinctly uncomfortable. Could I have done it for ten years, just to fake it for an insurance company? The question was as ridiculous as it ought to have been, and ought to be to anyone who really troubles to understand how people with MCS suffer. Once again, in addition to the physical suffering, the mental burden of being doubted and disbelieved is probably as damaging, certainly as hard to bear.

*

Susie had a catchphrase.

'I wonder what will happen next.'

She said it all the time; so often, I started to watch out for it, and for how she was using it.

'I wonder what will happen next.'

As if she was reading a book, or watching a film. But no, it was just life that was unfolding before our eyes, and Susie was commenting on it as you might comment on a football game.

It didn't need to refer to anything big, or dramatic. It might be some tiny thing that had just happened, and out it would come; 'I wonder what will happen next.' Sometimes, nothing at all had happened, and yet Susie would say, from nowhere, 'I wonder what will happen next.'

It has to mean something, I decided. This verbal tic; this little mental stutter. It must have evolved in her for a purpose of some kind; it must be aiding her in some way.

I wonder what will happen next. What finer expression could there be of the state that we all live in; doubt? None of us know what's going to happen next; not really, not deeply, not all the time. In that case, why not be honest about it? Why not wonder out loud about it? And I saw there was a big difference between Susie's catchphrase and the close alternative, of saying; 'I don't know what's going to happen next.' That admits to the fear; that rather implies we're *worried* that we don't know.

No. Susie had it spot-on; it seemed she'd accepted the Doubt, come to terms with the Not Knowing, and she had the right way of expressing it, a way that on the one hand admits that we live in ignorance, yet casts it merely as a thought, as an observation, not as fear.

I wonder what will happen next.

There was not even really the hint of a question mark on it. Every time she said it, I smiled inside. But I was about to stop smiling for some considerable time, because what happened next was that life decided to prove it has a better sense of humour than most of us have bargained for.

What happened next was that, having gone to the desert to talk to a bunch of sick people about their illness, I got sick with something else entirely, and as it turned out, fairly serious. Bacteria had decided to raise their tiny heads again. By Saturday morning, I was in ER in New York.

13 – La Peste

'Oui, nous avons trouvé quelque chose d'intéressante.'

Dr Mugnier was away when I finally got back home to France. I was seeing a summer intern, young and friendly.

'Ah, oui? Et c'est quoi?'

'C'est une infection bacteriologique.'

That is indeed, I thought, interesting.

'Oui, ça s'appelle Yersinia Enterocolitica. C'est plutôt rare. C'est une cousine de Yersinia Pestis.'

I was getting lost.

'Yersinia..?'

'Yersinia Pestis. La Peste.'

I blinked. He took it as a sign my French was failing me and kindly switched to English.

'La Peste. The plague. Er, you call it, the Black Death, I think.'

I blinked again.

'But don't worry, it's only a cousin; it's not the same thing.'

So, that was the good news, I didn't have the plague.

What they had found on my return to France, that they hadn't found when I was in hospital in New York, was that I had somehow picked up a 'rather rare' bacterial infection on my trip to Snowflake.

No one probably wants to read the details of this malady; so I'll keep it brief, and anyway, it was fairly simple. It was diarrhoea. The worst I'd ever had in my life. That first night, still sleeping on the porch at Susie's, I'd had to rush out of my sleeping bag and into the desert somewhere in a frantic scramble. After seven, I lost count of the number of trips I'd made, ignoring all thoughts of any rattlers and scorpions I might be squatting over. Poor them, as someone wittily said, later; something everyone found funny but me.

The next morning I'd had to sheepishly explain to Susie what had been going on, and asked if she'd drive me to the airport. I was sorry, but I had to cut the trip short. She was sweet, really sympathetic, and yes, of course she'd drive me to the airport. I got a seat on a new flight, Show Low to Phoenix, Phoenix to New York, before coming home. By some miracle, the trips to the bathroom held off for seven hours of the flight from Phoenix to New York; I guess the tank was empty. But that night, it all kicked off again. Six trips to the bathroom, seven, eight. I lost count, and the next morning I was on a drip in ER to get rehydrated.

The solution, of course, without even knowing what was wrong, was antibiotics. Strong ones. Two different kinds.

I started popping them like candy that afternoon, and very quickly, they seemed to have done the trick. Things returned to normal. More or less. Again, no one wants details of this, but matters weren't quite right. But at least I wasn't losing fluids so badly anymore, and the trips to the bathroom were drastically reduced.

I wrapped up the trip to the States and got back to France; I thought I'd maybe see if the doctor wanted a sample from me, since things were still not normal. And so I got the news that I had La Peste. Well, its distant cousin. The two courses of antibiotics had not been enough, it seemed. The young intern prescribed a third course, with the advantage this time of knowing what it was he was trying to kill.

I took it, and, bingo, everything stopped, everything *almost* normal, and if not quite clockwork, not far off.

*

A week went by. Ten days. I was due in the UK to work on two five-day writing retreats, back to back. Since things seemed

164

okay, I took my flight, caught a train to the West Country, took a taxi out to the retreat centre, met Charlie, the woman running the courses.

The student writers arrived. We had dinner. I went to bed. And then it all started again; the trips to the bathroom, six, seven, eight times. I was tired all the time anyway; this loss of fuel and fluid only made me weaker. Again, I had to sheepishly explain what was happening, and the totally unflappable Charlie kindly ran me to the local doctor's surgery, where, not being a local, and not living in the UK anymore, they wouldn't see me. The best they could do, they explained, was let me give a sample for analysis.

I did so. Within a few swift hours they phoned me, urgently.

'Ah, yes. We've found something...'

*

Not a return of La Peste; that was the good news. The bad news was that it was something potentially worse; a thing called *Clostridium Difficile*, often just referred to as C. Diff, often referred to as a super-bug. (As the weeks wore on, I started to joke to people that there was nothing 'super' about it at all. For some reason, only I seemed to find this joke funny.)

C. Diff is one of those bacteria causing the medical world some concern, because it can be very hard to get rid of. It causes unpleasant things such as diarrhoea, fever, nausea, and abdominal pain in the short term, and can lead to chronic problems if treatment is not successful; things like colitis, sepsis, and perforation of the colon. It can kill, particularly older and weaker individuals.

I was unamused to find I had an illness on top of an illness, but at least this time, I knew what was wrong. The only question was: what to do about it?

'So,' I asked the doctor who'd phoned me up during the second afternoon of the writing retreat, 'this was caused by taking antibiotics, is that right?'

'Yes, the antibiotics you've taken are a fairly nuclear option; they kill everything down there, indiscriminately; good bacteria and bad. This can lead to overgrowth of some particularly unpleasant and particularly resistant strains.'

'So what's the cure?'

'Antibiotics.'

I wasn't thrilled by this answer, it has to be said.

'And what's the chance of success, as opposed to yet even super-er bugs?'

'About 60%.'

'Oh,' I said. 'Well, sign me up.'

*

As it happened, I already knew a bit about C. Diff already, thanks to all my nerdy reading about bacteria. Whatever else antibiotics are starting to be accused of, their implication in the outbreaks of resistant bacteria and nasty things like the one I had were already well-established. In our well-intentioned desire to use antibiotics to (often successfully) alleviate the suffering from things like tuberculosis, syphilis, and so on, we have inadvertently caused a whole new range of things to suffer from. This is the summary of books like *10% Human* and *The Mind-Gut Connection*. Doctors have been warning for years about the dangers of the overuse of antibiotics, and of the danger of not finishing the whole course of the drugs; these things have been helping to breed antibiotic-resistant bacteria. Scientists have not been able to keep producing new, effective antibiotics as fast resistant strains have been developing, and the new strains are often more deadly than their forerunners. We face a return, very soon, to the pre-antibiotic days, and we will no longer have recourse to the 'magic bullet' for things we now take for granted as easily treatable. Stand back a little, and you can see that for a short space of time, we have been able to benefit from antibiotics; with the consequent drop in infant mortality, and mortality in general. My own father was born fully twelve years before Alexander Fleming's accidental discovery and naming of penicillin; it's possible that within my lifetime, it will largely become ineffective.

C. Diff is a little warning sign of the shape of things to come. There's that 60% chance you can fix it with more antibiotics, but if not, then what? One of the things I had been reading about, in the year before I went to Snowflake, was a rather radical-sounding solution to non-antibiotically treatable C. Diff infections; a thing known as FMT, which stands, rather alarmingly, for Faecal Microbiotic Transplant. If you're thinking that means what you think it does; yes, you're right: you whizz up someone else's stools in a blender, and syringe them into your colon, rectally.

There's growing interest in FMT as a possible cure for all sorts of problems; and given that we now know how important a healthy gut microbiome is for health in general, that makes sense. You can try to improve the health of your gut by changing your diet, by taking pro-biotics and eating more pre-biotic food, but if these things are still not enough to sort matters, you can take a more radical step – have a healthy person's microbiome put into your gut, to reset the bacterial balance therein. It's actually pretty simple, because much of the solid products of digestion that doctors like to call stools are bacteria; around 30%. The rest is undigested food; cellulose, fats, cholesterols, proteins, and so on. So, the idea is that you take the stools of a healthy person, and introduce them into your own little world; the bacterial balance is restored, and off you go. But *before* you go off and try this in the comfort of your own home, a word of warning.

There's a lot of controversy around FMT. This is not some new-age, flaky pseudo-science that is harmless but basically ineffective. The results of FMT can be dramatic. It's being used for things like IBS, for example, and – it's claimed – successfully. I had read about it, I'd heard it touted as a possible aid for people like me, with CFS. I'd got as far as looking up a UK-based clinic who practise it; and it is very advisable that you have it done by a sound clinic, since it's very important that the donor's stools are screened properly. There have been cases of people being made more ill through transplants of other people's faecal matter; guts are delicate things, and what's fine in one body may not be in someone else's. There have been cases of fat people being made thin after the transplant of a thin person's microbiome. There have been cases of thin people being made obese. There are even reports of personality changes – such is the power that these bacteria can have on our 'second brain'. So it's very advisable that you get a really healthy transplant, but even then, the jury is far from out as to whether it's an effective treatment for many of the issues for which great claims are being made.

In the US, the use of FMT has been banned for everything save for one type of intervention; for a C. Diff infection that is not responding to antibiotics, and it is so effective that it has out-performed all other approaches to this really stubborn problem, one which is causing misery and even death.

But finding a healthy microbiome to borrow from in the modern western world of fast food and fast medicine is the tricky part. It's the main obstacle preventing wider use; only about 1 in 100 potential donors meet the strict criteria, one of which, for example, is that the donor must never have taken antibiotics in their entire life. Not once. Ever since I had I read that, I had been trying to find someone who had never had antibiotics. It took me eight months of randomly asking friends and acquaintances, and eight months of funny looks, to find someone. Coincidentally, that person was Charlie, the woman running the very writing retreat where I suddenly came down with the C. Diff. But even then, I wasn't about to ask her for a 'donation' to improve my health; there was the other, tablet-borne approach to try before the syringe-borne one, so despite the risks, I took the fourth course of antibiotics in as many weeks, and prayed I would be in the 60% success camp. I was.

*

Which was great. I was back to having just the one, undiagnosed illness. What came next is hard to write about, not because it's any more or less traumatic, or dramatic than anything that has gone before, but just because everything became a bit of a mess. I started getting dragged down corridors of hope, in several different directions at once, trying to find the answer. I started to actually do some research into my old question of whether writers in particular, and creative people in general, are more prone to sickness. And still I was wrestling with the split over whether this illness was all in my head or all in my body.

14 – The Day I Woke Up
As A Lizard

'If I couldn't cure myself, perhaps I could at least begin to understand myself.'

So says Siri Hustvedt in her book, *The Shaking Woman*, in which she recounts the history of her own mysterious, undiagnosed illness. That seemed like good advice. I could already see cracks opening up in my mind, in my personality; small glimpses behind the curtain of who I was, or maybe, who I thought I'd been. I had already tried many therapies; both physical interventions and talking cures, all pretty much ineffective, it must be said. So what was starting to break the shell of my understanding of myself? It was the illness itself. As much as I hated to admit it, after four years of illness, it was true that I had started to become someone else; and I began to see things about myself that I had never known. And maybe one thing I'd tried had played a part in this process; and that was meditation.

*

We've all had the feeling of waking up and not knowing where we are. Some people might also recognise a rarer sensation; of waking up and not knowing *who* you are. That's happened to me a few times in my life, not for very long, it's true, and not as a result of heavy drinking or drug-taking. It's a strange feeling, to be awake, and not remember your name, or identity or personality. But at least you know you're still human, and I say that because just once, when I was a teenager, I had a whole different level of not knowing; because there was the morning I woke up and never mind where I was, or who I was, I didn't know *what* I was.

It was fleeting, over in a moment, but it was such a powerfully weird sensation that I have never forgotten it. I can only describe it in these terms. It was as if I was one level deeper than the 'who am I?' feeling, and two levels deeper than the 'where am I?' one. This 'what am I' feeling was something else entirely. To use the modern computer analogy we often apply to the brain, it felt as if the hardware was running, but no software had been loaded yet. To put it another way, it felt as if the oldest part of the brain was running; the evolutionarily primary, primitive brain; that part of us sometimes known as the lizard brain.

All I knew was that I was a living thing. I could sense the sheets against my body and the warmth of the room as I lay on my stomach, face turned slightly to the side. I knew it was dark. I knew I was an animal, that I had things that were both needs and desires, impossible to distinguish between the two. But that was about it, and absolutely none of these thoughts had words attached to them.

As I said, it passed in a matter of moments, as the very weird sensation of watching the other, 'higher' consciousnesses kick in. First, I remembered I was a human being; then which human being I was, my name and so on; then I recalled I was lying in my bed, at home. Then I went and had breakfast, set off for school.

It hadn't been disturbing; it had lasted too short a time for that, but it's stayed with me. Thinking back, I don't know which came first, but I know it was around then – maybe 14 or so – that I first tried meditation.

Now, at the time, being a sucker for all sorts of 1970s weirdness (this was the early 80s, but I was always slow to develop), I had bought a book called something like *The Secrets of Chinese Meditation*, and I think I had bought it expecting that I would probably be able to learn to levitate, or lift rocks with my mind, or something equally useful to a teenage boy. My life was pretty empty as a teenager – I filled it somewhat desperately with anything that promised a hint of something more beautiful or mysterious or fulfilling or exciting than anything that was actually happening to me in a rural corner of England with a hideous government ruling the land and hideous boys ruling my school.

Even if I'd already bought that book, and had tried meditation by the time Lizard Morning happened, I don't think for one minute it had anything to do with that practice. I suspect it was more to do with the vast amount of sleep I needed as I finally had a late growth spurt – a waking of some parts of the brain while others were having a much-needed teenage lie-in. But I do think it was interesting. It was as if I had had the ultimate goal of meditation (and if you practise meditation yourself, forgive my sloppy use of totally un-Zen things like 'goal') displayed to me, just once, shining and glittery like a big gold cup. Wasn't this what I was supposed to be doing? Thinking nothing? Lights on, nobody home?

Back to the now, I'd read that the single most effective 'treatment' to aid recovery from CFS was meditation. It wasn't much more effective than that 15% spontaneous recovery rate, but it was. Just. And it was free and safe. The only concern for me was why meditation was the most effective of the long list of admittedly not very effective cures. If meditation fixed it... didn't that play right into the hands of the all-in-your-head gang? But desperation will take you to some strange places; it had already taken me to try Reiki and Homeopathy, neither of which I have much faith in, rightly or wrongly. And there was nothing to be lost. So I began to meditate again.

By now, I had read a bit more about meditation. I'd learned it wasn't necessarily a question of thinking nothing; that it could be more a question of allowing thoughts to arise, and then allow them to pass away again just as easily, like leaves floating downstream. I knew it wasn't helpful to set goals, or time limits, or curse 'bad' days, or congratulate yourself over 'good' sessions. You just had to do it, and stop attaching things to it.

Oh boy.

Here I was again, all in my head, yet trying not to be, trying to be in my body. Or nowhere. Watching myself breathe, trying to let the thoughts go, noticing how noisy it all was up there in my skull; going through the thoughts that everyone who has ever tried to meditate has gone through: "Oh, there it is! Yay! I'm not thinking! Oh shit. Well, try again..." on and on in an endless cycle till the bell pings on your stupid phone.

*

I know I meditated daily for several months. Maybe six. Whatever else it did, I was still ill, physically. That became clear. Gradually, I fell away from the practice. Should I have kept it up? Was it helping? Would I have eventually got well? I don't know the answer to these questions.

Neither do I know why I stopped. I could spare the time; I had too much time, if anything, now. It wasn't hurting me, I told myself, so why did you stop? I still do it from time to time, just not every day as I had been. It helps a little; it keeps me calmer, but it's never made a direct difference to my fatigue.

On top of which, I knew there had arisen an equation in me; it was a complicated equation, and I can't tell you all of the arguments in it, but one of them was hope. And another was mental energy. Another may have been a different form of fatigue: one in which I got tired of trying things to not be tired. For whatever reason, the factors in this equation meant that I slowly stopped. Because maybe, as I said before, it's the hope that kills you.

*

As I stopped meditating every day, I started to become aware of something else about my personality; not only did I find it hard to stick at things beyond a certain point, which was in itself odd given what I thought I believed about my determination, I also started to recognise that I had always found it very hard to believe. In anything. For any amount of time.

Around this time, I wrote to a cousin of mine. I was feeling bad because he was one of the people I had allowed to slip slightly out of my life, and I still didn't really know why. We had been close for years, ever since we got divorced around the same time; we'd become much closer, though we had always wound each other up too, even as kids. There'd been a period of time when we'd almost completely lost touch, when he was married to an Evangelist's daughter; but when that marriage broke down, and my first had, we'd been good for each other. We'd been in touch a little bit by email, recently, so now, on this occasion, I wrote to Guy to ask him about Faith. Though no longer a born-again Christian, he was still religious, and I wanted to know a simple thing to ask, but probably an impossible thing to answer: what does it feel like to believe in something?

What does it feel like to consistently have faith? As we know, faith is not something that you have through evidential proof; it's just something you either have, or do not. I wasn't even looking for a religious angle here; for what was occurring to me was that I had little belief in me about anything. Above all, I had no belief that I would ever be well again, and the 'all-in-your-head' part of me was wondering whether that very belief was preventing me from recovering. There's a good line in the surprisingly-not-terrible-for-a-remake 1994 version of *Miracle on 34th Street*. Playing Kriss (with two Ss for some reason) Kringle, Richard Attenborough tells Elizabeth Perkins' character, who utterly discounts the idea of Santa Claus, "If… you can't believe, if you can't accept anything on faith, then you're doomed for a life dominated by doubt."

Doubt, which possibly does more damage in the long run than Faith, even, even if Faith is delusional. There can be good delusions, after all. Sometimes they are called religions. They were what used to take away that awful teenage existential angst for many people, and still do in the majority of the world, and, if you're able to, believing a delusion is more comfortable than staring at the alternative, nihilist nothingness. Virginia Woolf's frozen landscape and dying sun. But only if you're able to. It seemed I wasn't made that way, and no matter how much I might want to, or need to, I wasn't about to start finding God now.

My cousin couldn't really give me much of an answer. You either believe or you don't; that was what he had to tell me. As for what it felt like to have faith, I still couldn't feel any myself. But I still wondered whether if only I could believe in something for long enough, in meditation, for example, or Dr G's vitamin treatment, or whatever it might be, that I might get better. The trouble was, perhaps, that I flip-flopped from one explanation, and therefore possible cure, of my illness from day to day. Sometimes several times in one day. Exhausting in itself.

*

If evidence were needed of this, I was looking everywhere for a cure, following all sorts of avenues, all without success. It became a bewildering time, of hope and fear, of optimism followed by crushing disappointment, and as I followed the path of physical explanations, I simultaneously followed the path of mental ones.

In the latter spirit, I read about the placebo effect. I bought a recently published book on the subject, fascinating in its own right, but which held a discussion of the placebo effect's dark twin; the nocebo effect, being the very real power of the brain to cause not health, but illness. Where placebo means 'I will please', nocebo means 'I will harm.'

The placebo effect is an extraordinary thing; it's so powerful that the majority of new drugs that pharmaceutical companies try to bring to market have a very hard time proving themselves to be more effective than it. To give one example, most anti-depressants struggle to out-perform placebo; it's questionable whether many of them, even such worldwide smash hits as Prozac, should even be on the market, being, as one observer has noted, just 'placebo with side-effects.'

Other extraordinary things about the placebo effect include the fact that it can work even when you tell the recipient that they are receiving a placebo, and that its efficacy also seems to be somewhat genetically determined, being related to which particular emanation of a certain gene you have – a thing called the COMT Val158Met Polymorphism. Since you inherit one expression of a gene from your mother, in addition to one from your father, there are four possible combinations. In the case of the COMT val158met polymorphism, what this means is you can be val/val, val/met, met/val, or met/met. Met/mets are the lucky ones – they're super responders to the placebo. Val/val respond the weakest. 50% of the population are either val/met or met/val – somewhere in the middle. (There are other strange correlations between these four groups and certain personality types – met/mets are super over-the-top people, always positive even if it seems a bit false, everything is always just dandy; they are also, on average, significantly less altruistic than the others. You may know someone like this.)

Nocebo is even less well understood than placebo, and its effects and even its existence are the subject of debate, but there is evidence, for example, that telling people the side-effects of drugs before they take them can make those side-effects more likely to appear. It's been suggested by some research that nocebo could be the rationale for things like electromagnetic hypersensitivity, but I wasn't about to write to my friends in

Snowflake to send them that research. For none of this is known for sure.

Nevertheless, could this be a mechanism that the all-in-your-head camp would pounce upon? That for some mixed-up, hidden reason, your brain has decided to make yourself ill, and this is the way it does it, using the nocebo? Is this how hypochondria works? You can think yourself ill? Some people even claim this is how things like voodoo curses might operate – you think yourself to death. Could this also be why writers and creative types are more prone to mental health problems, and maybe even physical health problems; that they are genetically more able to think themselves into un-health?

As usual, there were no firm answers in the academic literature – it was just yet one more thing to think about. The research on nocebo is fascinating, but there's a long way to go as yet. Meanwhile, while getting bogged down in this stuff, I had opened a side-door into genetic factors; yet another avenue to explore.

*

Methylation is a biochemical process in which a methyl group, that is to say one carbon and three hydrogen atoms, becomes attached to a substrate such as neurotransmitters, hormones, immune cells, in order for them to complete a wide range of bodily functions, from immune system response to energy production to cell repair to detoxification, and many other things. In terms of energy production, the methylation cycle feeds into a fiendishly complicated web of other processes, such as the Kreb's cycle you may remember from school Biology. In short, the methylation process can sometimes become faulty – the result is either over-methylation or under-methylation, and what had caught my eye is that there is a distinct and peculiar list of physical and mental symptoms associated with each. Reading through the list of undermethylation had rung a few bells; in fact, it seemed to describe me, pretty closely.

The list includes many rather general traits such as perfectionism, obsessive tendencies, high libido, self-motivation and so on, but also a few rather specific physical things, such as stretch marks on the back, which I have. I ticked off more symptoms than not, and felt it was worth following up, since poor methylation can lead to fatigue.

This is relatively new science and there's every chance your GP won't be able to talk to you about it. In fact, as it turned out, I only managed to find one nutritionist in London who could discuss it, and to get tested she dispatched me to Dublin, where Dr O would take the blood. So I made an appointment with Dr O, and took a plane to Ireland. Dublin is a great city, but I saw little of it: Dr O's surgery was in a suburban semi-detached house to the south of town. I caught a cab out there and was met by Dr O's son – they're a double act – and waited to meet this doctor on the cutting edge of biochemical medicine.

The older Dr O was a sweet man; in his seventies, I'd guess. He shuffled me into his consulting room and took some notes. His accent was soft and gentle and, at times, hard to understand; when for a moment I didn't hear what he said, it took me a moment to grasp that he was asking if I had depression. If I had suicidal tendencies. He asked in the same tone of voice in which he'd just asked if I had any children.

He repeated himself; I nodded.

'Sure, it's a terrible thing isn't it?' he said, sadly. 'A terrible thing.'

I felt bad. I didn't want to make this kind old doctor sad; I just hoped he could make me well. He took the blood he needed and then told me he needed a urine sample too. I hadn't expected this and wasn't feeling I had much to give. Still, I took a pot and went to find the bathroom. Ten minutes later, I came back with a pitiful half-full container; Dr O assured me it would be enough, and poured some of it off into another plastic tube, currently without a lid. He set the tube upright on the countertop and set off hunting for a lid for it, the hem of his jacket swinging dangerously close to knocking over the hard-won sample.

As it turned out, I had to wait some weeks for the results because there was nowhere in either Ireland or the UK which did methylation testing – my samples were sent to the States, to Chicago, where they were tested not only for methylation status but also the presence or otherwise of something else new I'd never heard of: kryptopyrroles.

I'm still unsure as to what they might be, but it turned out I didn't have them anyway. As for methylation, yes, I was under-methylated. Not hugely, but enough for Dr O and the original nutritionist to put me on a new program of supplements designed to rebalance the methylation cycle.

There was a catch, however. There was a complicating factor, and that was the presence of a gene I came to call the motherfucker gene. Its real name is methylenetetrahydrofolate reductase, but some joker decided its best acronym would be MTHFR. I've since discovered I'm not the only one using this alternative name for it. Now, this part is edging into less-verified science, but different expressions of this gene have been implicated in a wealth of health problems and it's thought that a defective MTHFR enzyme can affect the methylation cycle.

*

If you're getting bored and confused by all this biochemistry, my work is done, for it is simply put here in the hope that you will believe me when I say that so was I. I had studied Biology at school, but this was beyond anything I cared to learn about. Even though it was about my health, and might just possibly hold the key to its improvement, I was finding it unbearable to go on studying this stuff. The more I read, the more complicated it became. I read about folate and histamine, and I read how some people are methyl-intolerant, which made things more complicated, because what I had to do was try to boost methylation. In order to find out that status, it would be necessary to get a genetic test done.

Fortunately, that part was relatively easy; these days, all you need to do is spit in a tube and four to six weeks later you will have your DNA sequenced. So I spat in a tube and what it showed was that yes, I also had the genetic variation making me methyl-intolerant. This meant using a more carefully controlled set of supplements than otherwise; for example, to consider just one supplement, that Vitamin B12 I'd been taking before? That turned out not to have been such a great idea, because the vast majority of B12 supplements are methylcobalamin; i.e., *methyl* B12. All those months of supplements I'd taken had probably been compounding the problem as much as fixing it. It took a while to hunt out a form of B12, which according to this protocol, I could tolerate: hydroxocobalamin.

*

I'll spare you the rest. The above is only here to give a merest hint of the long, complicated, confusing and frustrating process. It was also fundamentally tiresome, because I really felt I had better things to do than become a biochemist. Or try to. I stuck at this stuff for long periods, finally becoming exhausted by it itself. As much as I wanted to be well, I also wanted to use what little energy I had on actually having a life of some kind. Of possibly even having fun, something which felt like an extremely distant memory.

One thing that this time gave me was a newfound respect for the doctors I had started to mistrust. I knew the human body was complicated, but only when you start studying a bit do you get any idea how complicated.

So I went on. I tried the new supplement protocol for several months, and yet again it seemed to make no difference at all. As before, I didn't even get worse, and it may sound odd but even that was disappointing, since it can be a positive sign in some cases that you are starting to detoxify as the methylation cycle kicks in properly again.

*

Life was even more confusing than before. I had found one answer – I was under-methylated – but it seemed I was unable to fix that, and now had many, many more questions than I'd ever had before. I was bewildered and bothered and it might have been nice to have been bewitched too, but sadly I wasn't. Not by anything. I wished I was an animal, free of all these human thoughts, all this conscious pain. Maybe not even that smart an animal, maybe something nice and primitive. I started to pray that I would wake up as lizard again, and this time for good. And then, every night, I started to pray I would not wake up at all.

15 – A Borderline Case

'You have to become your own doctor,' that's what Susie in Snowflake had told me, and many others have since. When orthodox medicine is done with you, you have to become the expert in your own illness. But there's a problem: self-diagnosis is a terrible thing. It can be dubious, dangerous and downright foolhardy – I knew that. But then, you become compelled to become your own doctor. By this time, four years into the illness, I was more or less done with the healthcare system in France, just as I had been in the UK, with one remaining matter being looked into. That matter comes a little later in the story, and by now Dr Mugnier had already suggested to me that in all probability my illness was 'psychogenique'. He didn't call it 'all in your head', and the way he said it had a notably different quality to it. There was no shame attached. He wasn't suggesting it was my fault in any way; that I was malingering. Just that it was something psychological that was emanating as fatigue. I could see he was genuinely sorry both for my illness and for his lack of success in finding the solution. He was, quite simply, kind about it, but as Diane O'Leary, the bioethicist who I spoke to told me much later, Dr Mugnier still had no more logical, or for that matter ethical, reason to jump from 'we don't know what's wrong with you' to 'it's all in your head' than Dr T had had right at the start.

*

So, for me, it was a case of going on with getting used to not getting used to it. Nevertheless, from time to time, I would come across yet another avenue to think about, and that was what happened next.

I've had depression on and off my whole adult life. Over the years, I'd seen a range of people to talk to about it, and a range of things to try to overcome it, with running being the only ever successful thing. I must have seen at least ten therapists, counsellors or psychiatrists over the years. Yet none of them had ever talked to me about Borderline Personality Disorder. But when I read the list of traits that define BPD for myself, I was astounded.

As I said above, self-diagnosis is a precarious thing. Yet so is diagnosis itself, the usual kind, where a doctor diagnoses you. Whether we're talking about mental issues of physical ones, diagnosis is often very hard to get right. Misdiagnosis, and lack of diagnosis, are more common in either sphere than we like to think. In fact, the level of Undiagnosis in general is much higher than you might expect; Dr Diane O'Leary had told me that recent figures for the UK estimate that fully 50% of all visits to the doctor result in an absence of diagnosis. If you find that surprising, or alarming, it may further surprise you to read of the work by Dr John Ioannidis, who's recently become well known for his studies claiming that the vast majority of all medical research is flawed, and by 'vast majority' he means up to 90% of it.[i] It might also alarm you to know that, in the field of psychology, less than 1% of experiments are ever replicated by other researchers.[ii] And yet it is on the basis of such things that the field of psychosomatic medicine sets out its camp.

I had already seen how hard it was for my doctors in the UK or France to come up with a physical diagnosis, other than CFS, which I had long ago abandoned as anything other than a mere description of my symptoms.

Mental diagnoses are possibly even harder. At least for physical things, there's a chance of finding a certain blood score, or a bacterium, or something else that is indisputable, objectively 'real'. The issue with the diagnosis of mental health disorders is that certainty is much harder to come by. I would be doing the field of psychiatry a great disservice if I tried to pretend that its proponents have not tried extremely hard to introduce some rigour and objectivity to their field, for they have, but that figure of 1% of experiments being replicated does not inspire great confidence.

One problem is that too many things are simply too subjective. Diagnosing mental health disorders has been reduced (and maybe that verb is unfair in itself, but I mean it in a neutral, perhaps even positive sense) to scoring a number of traits on a checklist. Self-assessed outcomes are notoriously unreliable, and are one of the many reasons the PACE trial was discredited.

To take just one example from psychiatry, psychopathy is defined according to how the prospective candidate scores on a thing called the PCL-R, sometimes known as the Hare Psychopathy Checklist - Revised, after Dr Robert Hare, who came up with it. In simple terms, it works like this; you're scored from 0 to 2 on a list of 20 different factors. The resulting score, which will therefore be somewhere between zero and forty, is totted up. If you score over 30, you're a psychopath.

So what's wrong with that?

Well, for one thing, say you score 29. If you score 29, you're technically not a psychopath. Good news. But only in the United States. If you're in the UK, the cut off is 25, so yep, you're crazy. That's a whopping 12.5% difference in scores. Are American psychopaths '12.5% different' from British ones? It seems unlikely.

For another thing, one can question (and people have) how accurate one can be in scoring the factors from 0 to 2. Factor one, for example, is "selfish, callous and remorseless use of others"; factor two is "chronically unstable, antisocial and socially deviant lifestyle". Just how objective can anyone be for these terms? Can you assign a number to such things? Of course, we're told, that's why it's not good to self-diagnose – clearly, it takes years of study and training to become expert in assessing things of this nature with clinical accuracy. But, and it's a pretty big but, maybe that's all just the Emperor's New Clothes. Maybe the psychiatry gang just have to maintain that they know what they're doing to present a unified face of best-practice science to us lay-folk. The validity of the PCL-R test for Psychopathy, for example, is widely disputed. True, it has become adopted as the global measure for psychopathy, but it has done so despite frequent methodological criticisms. In 2010, Hare went to court to try to prevent a peer-reviewed paper from being published, one that heavily criticised the PCL-R. Eventually, the paper was published. It argued that the PCL-R leaves out key factors, makes criminality too central and that it gives rise to over-diagnosis. Further, Hare conceded later, he receives tens of thousands of dollars in royalties a year from its use, which can obviously be argued as impacting his impartiality. Yet, for all its faults, the PCL-R is still what most practitioners use and believe to be valid; largely for want of any alternative.

The bible of all mental health diagnosticians is the DSM, or Diagnostic and Statistical Manual of Mental Disorders, now in its fifth incarnation as DSM-5, published in 2013. DSM-I (they used Roman numerals for the first four editions) was published in 1952, and a short stroll through the biography of this massively powerful book reveals a little – both about the changing nature of our understanding of mental health and our society as a whole. Witness the fact that in that 1952 edition, homosexuality was listed as a sociopathic personality disturbance. That may have been the early fifties, but for many, the DSM still has a lot of growing up to do. To give one controversial example, transvestism is still listed; as a 'paraphilic disorder'. Think about that. If, as a man, you decide to dress your legs in one tube of cloth rather than two, you're deemed crazy. Isn't *that* crazy? Other people question its basic premise, being by design focussed on the emergent symptoms rather than on any underlying causes. But it's still the Bible when it comes to diagnosing mental health disorders.

All this is a lengthy preamble to say that I knew what I was toying with in home-diagnosing Borderline Personality Disorder. But a quick read of the traits associated with it, and later much more in-depth reading about it, and it seemed it was at least possible that, well, that it was me. I was also struck by the (not) irony of being a writer and possibly having something labelled 'borderline' because writers spend their working lives negotiating their characters' liminality, their borderline states.

There are nine key traits on the BPD checklist; I ticked off most of them.

It wasn't just the checklist, but reading books written by people with BPD and those living with people with BPD, that reinforced the feeling that maybe this was who I was. I felt a strange sense of relief. That there were other people who felt like I did about the world, even if we got tagged with a 'disorder' as a result. That there were other people whom the world generally deemed to be 'too sensitive'.

But this wasn't good enough. You can't self-diagnose; you really shouldn't. Instead, I took it as a thing to be investigated, so I did. I found a renowned, trained psychotherapist, someone who specialised in BPD, and went through my 'case notes' with him. To cut this story as short as I can, it turned out that while I have much of the same feelings as those with BPD, I cannot be truly said to be BPD myself, according to the scores he took. The most we can say, he told me, is that I am borderline Borderline. Maybe, as with psychopathy, my scores might have been enough to classify me if I lived somewhere else, but not according to this psychotherapist, at least. Of course, these things are always a spectrum, and so I guess I am on that spectrum somewhere, a little closer to the BPD end than the end that says 'totally normal person without a hint of madness'. Yet, still, it was somehow enormously comforting that I am not just 'crazy'; that there are reasons why I'm made the way I'm made; that I had some kind of diagnosis, unlike with whatever was physically wrong with me.

*

To return briefly to the previous chapter, there are some interesting thoughts to be added while we're talking about diagnosing mental health issues. I pointed out that with things of the mind, it's never as simple as taking a blood sample and counting. But what if it could be, in some cases at least? What if you could put a number to a cause of a form of depression, objectively? This is where the research about methylation comes back into the story. Methylation and its relevance to various mental imbalances has been the life work of Dr William Walsh. Over many years, Dr Walsh worked with thousands of extreme cases; violent offenders imprisoned for their behaviours, and found that there were relationships between certain personality types and particular nutrient imbalances in that person, for example in levels of zinc, or copper, or those kryptopyrroles, or the methylation status. He has had spectacular results in treating stubborn cases, extreme cases, simply by correcting various nutrient levels. He has identified five basic depression biotypes: undermethylation; folate deficiency/overmethylation; copper overload; pyrrole disorder; and toxic overload, which in all account for 95% of depressions. Each biotype has a particular set of moods and behaviours connected to it, as well as other traits such as levels of fatigue, hirsutism, libido. Associated treatment plans can be prescribed for each type, using the appropriate nutrients. These are big claims, and it's still work in progress, but I found it reassuring to see someone pulling actual measurable science, and effective solutions, out of the vast ineffable swamp that depression and other mental health disorders usually feels like.

If it's true that there's a link between certain biochemistries and things like depression, and things like fatigue, then I realised this put a very different spin on the all-in-your-head argument. The causality is entirely changed. Rather than a causality that runs 'you are tired because you are depressed', it's possible there's a different one which says 'both your depression and your fatigue are emanations of a third, hidden thing: a chemical imbalance in your body and brain'. And at this point, the rug is pulled out from under the feet of the 'all in your head' gang. Their argument becomes stupid, irrelevant, meaningless.

The difference is massive. I cannot overstate this. It overturns the whole business; and it takes guilt and blame away from the sufferer. For as much as the orthodox health services in the UK and the US like to state that we should no longer stigmatise the mentally ill, there are still plenty of doctors and other practitioners who are only too free to imply, or openly state, such things. The 'malingerers' group is out there, and I'd run into a couple of them myself; albeit in a minority, but a damaging minority.

*

I decided it was time to try to get some actual answers, and I wanted to start with almost the first thing I'd heard about ME/CFS when I had been given that label; that people who get it are very often of a certain personality type: 'type A's, high achievers, perfectionists, and so on. I realised that because that seemed like a reasonable description of me, I had just accepted it at face value. I'd been told the story of Florence Nightingale, for example. Everyone knows about the incredible effort Florence Nightingale put into the care of soldiers during the 19th century, working hard to improve sanitary conditions both in the barracks and in the field hospital. Many people know that she was famous for her hard work; the long hours she put in; how she worked... well, I was about to write tirelessly, but that would have been a bad word choice. For Florence Nightingale did get tired. In fact, on her return from the Crimea, her health was a mess; she kept on trying to work, and kept brow-beating others into helping her, though she herself had become an invalid. She had some ups and downs health-wise from then, but the main trajectory was down – she lived the final fourteen years of her life in her bedroom. It's now being suggested that she had CFS, and a big part of the rationale for that lies as much in an analysis of her personality type as it does of her symptoms. And this, despite the fact that she may equally possibly have been suffering from a bacterial infection called Brucellosis.

So, I wondered; is it actually true – are some personality types more like to get CFS than others? I wrote to a well-respected ME charity and support group in the UK, the ME Association, to see what their official position was. The ME Association is a great resource for anyone wanting to read the actual science that's been done into ME/CFS. Every month, they update an index of all major research that has been done into the illness, most of it available to read online.

The answer to the 'personality type' question tuned out to be that there isn't much actual evidence for any correlation. There have been a couple of papers trying to show a link between 'perfectionism' and CFS; for example one[iii] which tried to make the case for a connection, and which fed into the UK's approach to treating ME/CFS through Cognitive Behavioural Therapy. It was on the basis of this work that NICE (the UK's National Institute for Health and Care Excellence) concluded that Cognitive Behavioural Therapy would remove unhelpful mental attitudes and so, therefore, make CFS sufferers better. The problem is, it just hasn't worked. There is no evidence that CBT is helping ME/CFS sufferers recover. The ME Association's view is that this is because the science isn't there; that there is no link between personality type and CFS.

In fact, the ME Association seem almost militantly opposed to any suggestion that there could be *any* mental component to CFS. Their online and general media presence is geared towards getting more of the outside world to believe that CFS is a physical, neurological disease. Their merchandise and ad campaigns are often oriented towards messages reinforcing the idea that ME/CFS is not 'in the mind' – for example T-Shirts printed with 'It's real... it's physical... it's ME' or leaflets stating 'I suffer from your inability to see my disability'.

It seems clear why this is their position. They are effectively in a war with the UK government, in the guise of NICE, to campaign for more research, for more funding into ME/CFS. That won't come while NICE believes it's an illness that is 'all in the mind'. If NICE were forced to change its position on ME/CFS, the financial burden would probably destroy the National Health Service, or cripple the government with debt in trying to not let that happen. As one doctor explained off the record to me, since 50% of all visits to the doctor result in an absence of diagnosis, there is an enormous financial impact of not knowing what is wrong with people; in the form of more tests, examinations, doctors' time. The quicker you can write a patient off as 'all in your head', the quicker the costs associated with them can be stemmed. In fact, she said told me, the greatest cost to the healthcare system is that of the undiagnosed. The best thing for them to do, from a short-term financial point of view, is give you some kind of diagnosis, no matter how unwarranted, how inaccurate, how unethical. Never mind the individuals left suffering, never mind the loss to the economy of hundreds of thousands of missing workers. And once you have the ME/CFS label, you'll be lucky to have any further form of intervention at all. Maybe a few weeks of CBT, for example, as I had; still infinitely cheaper than ongoing years of tests that find nothing. There are very powerful forces operating behind this rationale, something I touch on more in the appendix to this book.

*

So, conversely, the danger of sufferers admitting that there is *any* mental aspect to the illness is allowing one foot in the door to the 'all-in-your-head' camp. Give them that inch, and the mile will soon follow. And money is the reason why, but I said *short term* point of view, financially-speaking, because the long-term cost to a country of losing people from the workforce is probably incalculable. In the face of the pandemic, and the explosion of the chronically ill that is already underway, all this needs to be more widely understood by the general public, and by those who decide how healthcare policy works.

*

I came away feeling that I utterly sympathised with the need of people like the ME Association to adopt the view we might call 'all in your body' in the face of the governmental behemoth they're struggling with, but also, I came away demoralised. For while this black and white, oppositional thinking continues, and in so doing denies that there might be other, subtler, more sophisticated causalities, it's probable that the real breakthrough will never come. In this battleground, with the 'body camp' on one side and the 'mind camp' on the other, there can be no room for discussions of things like Dr Walsh's biotypes, for example, in which a physical thing, namely biochemistry, causes both physical symptoms (fatigue) and mental symptoms (depression). Even if Dr Walsh's work is never fully accepted, I was starting to become more and more sure that part of the complexity of CFS is that it's rooted in something in which both physical and mental factors play their part. I didn't have much evidence for this, save what my gut feeling(s) had been telling me – that it could be both. That it probably is something of both. At the very least, even if ME/CFS is a physical illness, with physical causes, I already knew from my own experience that stress makes the symptoms worsen. And if that stress is coming from not being taken seriously by the very doctor who you're turning to for help, then that would be a bitter pill indeed. Research funded by the ME Association themselves, shows that how the illness is treated in its early stages has a significant correlation with its length and severity, concluding, "The proportion of respondents reporting a bad relationship with their GP was significantly higher among severe cases than mild ones, both before and after diagnosis. It is clear that a good relationship with the GP from the outset of the illness is very important in achieving a good outcome and avoiding severe illness."[iv]

It's this simple: imagine being ill, sicker than you have ever been in your life, and the very person you turn to for help tells you you're imagining it. The stress of that alone is deeply damaging.

*

As for a good relationship with the GP... Well, I thought, I suppose it had just been my bad luck that my usual doctor had been on sabbatical when I became ill. Would that really have made any difference, if Dr Beattie had been there, rather than the Dr T and her 'all in your head', and Dr K and his startling absence of bedside manner? I didn't know, but I did know how much the reception of these first two doctors had affected me, even shocked poor little nervy me, when I turned to them for help. Whether that had prolonged or deepened the severity of my illness is an experiment that can never be run, but it did raise a rather nagging issue for me, in terms of the ME Association's view of CFS as being 100% physical. If that were the case, why would your relationship with your doctor affect it? I think it's very simple; because stress makes all illnesses worse.

*

Yet, still more unknowns. As ever, the more I read, the more I learned that I had very little idea what was going on, not only with me, but with the wider subjects that my illness had brought me into. If there was no truth in the old tale that ME/CFS patients have a certain, nervy personality type, then what about that other story, that everyone knows to be true, that creative people are more prone to madness, to depression? Not for the first time, I felt it was time to find some facts.

---

[i] Ioannidis JP. Why most published research findings are false. *PLoS Med.* 2005; 2(8):e124. doi:10.1371/ journal.pmed.0020124

[ii] This told to me by author and psychologist Professor Brian Hughes, PhD.

[iii] Brooks SK, Chalder T, Rimes KA. Chronic Fatigue Syndrome: Cognitive, Behavioural and Emotional Processing Vulnerability Factors. Behav Cogn Psychother. 2017 Mar;45(2):156-169. doi: 10.1017/S1352465816000631. Epub 2017 Jan 18. PMID: 28098051.

[iv] https://www.meassociation.org.uk/wp-content/uploads/2013/04/Biology-and-Medicine_Published-paper_vol1_4_50-74.pdf

16 – The Write Stuff

I feel it's safe to say this, since I am a writer myself: the very essence of writing is selfishness. Maybe that's a negative spin; maybe self-absorbed would be slightly better. Better still, perhaps they're just self-driven; something internal is what forces them to sit down and write 100,000 or 150,000 words about some dumb subject or other, such as their personal experience of chronic undiagnosed illness, for example.

In discussing writing, I often point out to people that in addition to that inspiration that people are always asking about are two other equally important things. Yes, the imagination is important, but I believe all people have an imagination; if only they would see it, or allow it to happen. We're very good at beating creativity out of people in society in general. But in addition to having an imagination, what you need to be a writer are two other essential qualities. The first is the ability to make connections, and that's something we'll come back to later. The second thing is obsession. You cannot sit in a room by yourself for months on end and write tens of thousands of words unless you are obsessed. Utterly, totally obsessed. And what that obsession inevitably entails is a certain degree of self-ness. I'm not necessarily talking about the practical matters of taking time you might have spent with your family to devote instead to writing, though there may have to be some of that selfishness too. I'm trying to suggest that the very impetus to write is something interior, utterly personal and unique to every writer. Writing is about the most self-indulgent thing I can think of.

Writers are introverts, by and large, even if some of them can also show extraversion when the time calls for it. By the nature of their work, writers are supposed to be profound students of interiority, of the depths of human nature; how else can they create believable, moving, gripping characterisations if they are not able to understand the fundaments of the psyche? And yet, the vast majority of writers I know show an extraordinary lack of self-awareness. I didn't always think this way; I used to idolise almost every writer I came across. Then I started to meet them, more regularly, more often, and I changed my mind.

I could fill the rest of this book with anecdotes about the appalling behaviour of writers I have met. The Booker Prize winner who dribbled gravy down his chin throughout dinner; the best-selling author at an award ceremony who stormed away from the table the moment the winner was announced and it wasn't him; the writer cheating on the woman he was already cheating on his wife with; the writer I'd just met who asked me directly how much I made from writing so she could gleefully tell me she earned more; the Beloved National Icon who berated an eight-year-old boy and reduced him to tears because he'd asked why said Icon's books had sad things in them; the bullying in award committee discussions; the continual jostling to be top-dog or queen bee; the only-ever-talking-about-your-own-work; the general bitterness, backbiting, gossiping; the arrogance masquerading as self-effacement; the humble-brags; the hideous, shameless self-promotion. Follow a writer on Twitter, and the chances are you'll unfollow them five minutes later. Maybe that's just people. And yes, I know some lovely, humble writers too, but they seem to be in the minority. Maybe that's just people too. But, all in all, one thing I have come to dread in life is being invited to have dinner with other writers, and that's weird, because I love talking about books, about how they work, and who made them, and why. I ought to love it, but instead, I know the chances are I'll be in for two hours of having someone try to passive-aggressively show that they're better than me in some admittedly inventive way. What underlies it all is insecurity, of course. What underlies it is that writers are nervy types; the sensitives. Thin-skinned canaries. This insecurity is the reverse side of a coin of which most people only see the obverse: the oozing confidence of the well-known, successful author.

It's rather sad how becoming a writer took the edge off my love of writers. In a similar way, I was a bookseller for three years, and later worked in publishing, experiences which I fundamentally loved, but which also fundamentally changed my relationship to books. I know many people who've worked in bookselling and publishing who feel the same. Before, books are a precious thing; each individual copy a minor miracle of some kind. After, they become 'product', they become commodities; they become units in the warehouse. They become the thing you're trying to achieve higher sales of; you start to lose sight of them as those tiny miracles. One day, when I had pressed *send* on an email to instruct the warehouse to send a huge number of books to be pulped, because they had not sold, I knew my relationship with books had changed, for I didn't feel like a murderer doing it. George Orwell knew this feeling, too, having been a bookseller, and wrote about it in an essay called *Bookshop Memories*. 'As soon as I went to work in a bookshop, I stopped buying books... I lost my love...'

I digress; the point is just that my view of writers had changed too; I had lost my love of writers *en masse*. At some point, I realised something. An image came to mind of how I viewed writers, before and after I knew a bunch of them. Before, I saw them as the famous figure on the mountaintop in Casper David Friedrich's *Wanderer above the Sea of Fog*; hair-blown by the winds of life, our hero strides the very mountaintops in order to bring us mere mortals the manna of understanding. Afterwards, the image was a little different. Picture a mechanical monkey, strapped to a high-speed clockwork toy train hurtling around a track, frantically masturbating with one hand while simultaneously throwing more track down in front of it with the other as it goes, to stay on course to nowhere. That's the best image of a writer I can imagine these days. Though, in saying this, the Egyptian God Thoth was both the deity of writing, and had one aspect in the form of a baboon. So maybe we can be both.

I'm no better. I recognise that insecurity underlies it all, but undoubtedly someone has a list of genuinely awful things to say about me, too, and no doubt of which I am guilty; my point is simply that writers are terrible people, and to live with one must take the patience of a saint. And for two writers to try to live together, surely that would be even worse.

And why? Because as everyone knows instinctively to be true, creative people in general, and writers in particular, are prone to mental health problems – and that in itself can make for difficulties in relationships. And, so the thinking goes, it's a two-way street, because maybe it's those very mental health problems that are the seed of the creativity; or its fuel. It's from these dark places that writers draw their energy to write; the beauty comes out of the horror, or some such cliché like that. More than a few times, I've had conversations with writer friends undergoing therapy, and while they very much wanted to not be depressed any longer, they were genuinely concerned in case the disappearance of their demons led to a disappearance of their creativity, monkey-on-the-track-style. I include myself in this list. But despite this ubiquitous worry, I have never seen it happen. Ever.

*

So is it true? As I mentioned in the first chapter of this book, isn't there well-established research that proves the link between madness and creativity? Well, as it turns out, the answer is the usual one to be found in this book: maybe, and then again, maybe not. In fact, there is very little good research proving such an association. There is some, but very often it's flawed methodologically. I hunted out as many academic papers as I could on the subject, in addition to personal accounts, newspaper and magazine articles; the more I looked, the more the certainty that writers are any more likely to be mad than anyone plucked at random from the general population seemed to crumble. The argument still rages; every year, more pieces come out on one side or the other – the only truth to be found is if you decide to pick a side and stick with it. But that takes Faith, something I don't have.

Of all the studies I read, the work that summed up the issues involved the most succinctly was by Christa L Taylor, PhD, in which she tried to unpick the complexity of the problem; and complex it is, for the problem is really not as simple as it might first appear.

To start with, there's the issue of definitions. It's one matter to say, in common parlance, 'writers are crazy'; it's quite another in clinical terms to explain what you mean by 'crazy'. If that were simple, the DSM-5 would not be 947 pages long. But it is. Almost a thousand pages cataloguing one form of 'madness' from another. The problem with much of the classic research into this question is that definitions are not clear; exactly which mood disorder (of many dozens) are you trying to prove is correlated with creativity? And secondly, what do you even mean by 'creativity'? And how are you going to judge whether someone is creative or not? Because they say so? Because they've won an award? (for writing, not for lunacy). Because they published a book? Does it have to be a published book? Does it have to be *good*? You only need scratch the surface of this widely-held belief to begin to see that it's far from clear.

Taylor explains the issues. Firstly, the whole thing might just be what's called an illusory correlation. We need to see past the assumption, which is one continually reinforced by popular culture and the media, in a process that is self-selecting, self-reinforcing. We hear a story about a crazy writer, and we add it to our collection of stories about crazy writers; but we hear one about a totally 'sane' writer and we forget it. 'Boring' does not sell; so biographies of utterly happy creatives simply do not end up on the shelves. When I spoke to Taylor about her work, she gave me just one example: in *The Insanity Hoax*, Judith Schlesinger recounted how various biographers abandoned projects about the saxophonist Bud Shank because there was simply no dirt to dish. And here's an example I stumbled across; in the introduction to his book about hypochondria and famous creative/high achieving types, *Tormented Hope*, Brian Dillon admits he abandoned the inclusion of one individual because he could not get past the 'sanitary cordon of his personality' – instead looking for someone the reader 'could identify'. Presumably, that there should be some dirt to dish. Put simply, why write a book about creative people who are happy? Who cares?

Taylor also explains that an illusory correlation can be reinforced by the thing known as the *availability heuristic*, namely that we make an estimation of how common something is by how easily we can bring examples to mind. And because stories of writers drinking Prussic Acid (step forward Dr John Polidori) or attempting to slit their throats and subsequently dying in an asylum (take a bow Guy de Maupassant) or gassing themselves and nearly their downstairs neighbour too in the process (hands up Sylvia Plath) or throwing themselves from the window of their apartments (yes, you, Gilles Deleuze) or Papa on his porch at Ketchum at dawn with his shotgun in his hands rather stick in the mind; we bring them more easily to mind than the fact that Chekhov died peacefully in his sleep, even if it was tuberculosis he was dying of.

In more concrete terms, Taylor's work drills down into the methodological problems of much of the existing research. For one thing, she says, 'the scientific study of creativity and mood disorders is limited. There are vastly more reviews and commentaries discussing why and how a relationship might exist than there are studies examining if there is a relationship at all."[i]

She explains that such research, as there is, falls into one of three categories. The first type compares mood disorders shown by creative people as opposed to less-creative people. The second compares the inverse: the creativity of people with mood disorders and those without mood disorders. The third type looks at whether mood disorders are correlated with creativity. She notes that each type can answer a different question, 'For instance... Do creative individuals have more mood disorders? is distinct from: Do individuals with mood disorders have more creativity? Erroneously drawing conclusions about the answer to one from evidence for or against the other is known as the fallacy of the inverse, which is very common in this line of research.'

In conclusion, having conducted meta-analyses of the extant research, Taylor argues that it is far from clear that there are significant correlations between mood disorders and creativity: 'because there is no agreed-upon objective way of measuring either one, the conclusions regarding their relationship end up being based on symptoms... No one would suggest that the flu is somehow linked to pregnancy, yet they can both cause fatigue, headaches and nausea.'

All that can really be said with any certainty is that there may be some small and very specific correlations. One of the experts in this field is Dr James Kaufman, who was Taylor's PhD supervisor. I spoke to Kaufman about his most famous piece of research, known as the Sylvia Plath Effect, which showed that female poets were more prone to mental illness than female fiction writers or male writers of any type. In his words, "That's a pretty esoteric finding – it's interesting in a cocktail party way, but people would interpret it very personally. But can you extrapolate, can you generalise? Sylvia Plath was a *very* accomplished poet. This does not mean that this correlation applies to everyone who is creative in an everyday fashion." And yet it has been, and still is, used to 'prove' the broad link between creativity and mental health, despite the fact that its own discoverer advises caution.

*

Once again, the question of unclear causalities had raised its head, as with my own experience of depression and chronic fatigue. Was I ill because I was depressed, as my doctors wanted to suggest, or was I depressed because I was ill, as had seemed much more logical to me? Or, as I had started to think was possible, were both the result of a third, unknown cause?

There is as much muddled thinking around issues like madness and creativity as there is around CFS and mental health, and all this is dangerous stuff. For one thing, telling people that creativity is all down to some connection with madness, i.e., something outside of their compass, may prevent many people from exploring their potential, potential that could give them a fulfilling life. And similarly, telling creative people that their successes are due to some dark madness could be damagingly invalidating, not only perhaps preventing the individual from seeking therapy as I have witnessed countless times with friends, but simultaneously removing any sense of achievement from an already possibly fragile sense of self and handing it instead to the Black Dog. If nothing else, it simply ignores the vast amounts of hard work that most successful creative people have expended.

There's a final corollary to this which is also irksome, to say the least, to someone trying to make their way in the fiercely competitive world of creative industries, such as publishing. I have often noted how some of our most successful writers sport an unusual physical adornment of some kind: Oh, that hat he always wears! The rings she sports! Those trousers! The beard! Whatever it may be. Does eccentricity help push the writer upwards? Are these things necessary to success? Rather appallingly to me, it appears they might be, and yet I still believe the greatest writers I know are the ones without these affectations. The ones who seem (almost) 'normal'.

Christa L. Taylor notes the study that showed that students being introduced to Van Gogh's *Sunflowers* for the first time rate it as a better piece of art if they were told the story of him cutting off his ear than if they were not; another study showed that a piece of art was priced more highly by those who were told – through a fictional biography – that the artist was 'eccentric.' A previous publisher of mine, who was getting great publicity for another of her authors on the basis of that author's disability, once bemoaned the fact there was 'nothing wrong' with me (this was years before illness arrived), as it would help her sell my books if there were.

Such things leave a sour taste in the mouth for those of us who would like to believe that the only thing that matters is the quality of the writing, and nothing else. Naïve perhaps; all writing, all art, in fact all culture is the domain of the human; is subject to the whims and bigotry and biases of all us of – those beings who can only ever be subjective, no matter how we might think differently. But galling, nonetheless, to those of us that live by how many copies of our books get sold, or how high our paintings are valued, or how many people fall for the tragic backstory behind the songs we sing.

*

So the answer to the question of whether writers are madder than most was, as always... maybe. But maybe, very possibly not. It was an answer I was all too familiar with, and yet it didn't stop me looking, because there was a further step I wanted to take; to find out whether writers are sicker than most, too – not mentally, but physically.

[i] https://aeon.co/essays/is-there-any-evidence-linking-creativity-and-mood-disorders

17 – Unlearning

Well. Here was something I was not expecting. I'd wanted to read the research into the question of whether writers (or more generally, creative people) are more prone to physical sickness than the general population. What I was expecting by now, of course, was a tide of papers showing 'yes' and others arguing 'no'. After all my induction into the school of not-knowing, I was expecting someone to have done the meta-studies which would conclude with the only rational answer possible to these most complex questions; i.e., 'maybe.' What I was not expecting was that the research didn't exist at all.

I found conferences devoted to the interactions of literature and medicine. There is even a journal with that very title, *Literature and Medicine*, which since 1982 has been issued at first annually and now bi-annually by John Hopkins University Press. It's full of extremely interesting pieces, such as these two, at random: *'Reading The Operation: Television, Realism, and the Possession of Medical Knowledge'* and *'Overwhelming the Medium: Fiction and the Trauma of Pandemic Influenza in 1918'*. Elsewhere, I found paper after paper looking at how literature has treated illness and medicine and the medical profession; of writing about doctors and by doctors, about patients and by patients. There are studies of how, and indeed whether, writing can help the sufferer cope with illness, or even help treat mental health problems. I even found a paper attempting to draw conclusions between my hero Thomas Mann's cause of death, an iliac arterial rupture, and the themes of his greatest work: *The Magic Mountain*. Again, all fascinating stuff, to me at least.

Yet nowhere could I find a single study of what I had again stupidly assumed would be a simple matter: do writers have weaker constitutions than the rest of the population? The answer for why this is may be obvious; if you attempt some searches into this question yourself, you'll see that no matter what you try, the results are dominated by the question of the previous chapter – the supposed relationship between creativity and *mental* health. So I couldn't even get a 'maybe' type of answer to this question, with one possible exception that I'll come to later.

*

Meanwhile, I had come across some other research that I found pertinent; research into the nature of creative people and the functioning of a part of the brain called the precuneus. I said in the last chapter that what's required to be a writer is more than an imagination; that it also takes obsession and, perhaps the least discussed factor of the three, the ability to make connections. E. M. Forster knew it, hence his famous motif from *Howard's End*: 'Only connect'. One quote from the book, in full:

'Only connect! That was the whole of her sermon. Only connect the prose and the passion, and both will be exalted, and human love will be seen at its height. Live in fragments no longer. Only connect, and the beast and the monk, robbed of the isolation that is life to either, will die.'

Here, Forster was talking about the importance of connecting in order to live well, but he may just have as well been discussing the centrality of connection to story-making, because stories come about not just because you have an imagination and the obsession to stick with it. Stories come about because you make connections; often because you make connections between things that may at first thought seem quite disparate. Unconnected.

The precuneus is a region of the brain thought to have a role in processes concerned with the sense of self, self-consciousness, and deep memory retrieval, amongst others. In the following, I'm going to sloppily use the word 'normal' to describe people who aren't writers; I hope you can forgive me, and I don't really mind if writers can't.

The precuneus shows its highest levels of activity during rest; that is to say, when the person is not engaged in an external task. It's been found that the quantity of grey matter in the precuneus increases in people who practice mindfulness. In 'normal' people, however, the precuneus is switched off once they engage in some activity or other. What a group of interrelated research over the last few years has shown is that, by contrast, creative people are unable to suppress, or have difficulty in suppressing the activity of their precuneus during such external interactions. Instead, it's basically switched on all the time. What this is thought to mean is that creative people are continually making connections between things. Given what the precuneus does, these connections will often be between a stimulus in the external world, and their own, deep sense of self, of personal memory. And if that isn't the most accurate (even if possibly the most boring) description of how a book comes into being, I can't imagine what is.

I want to repeat this: the precuneus *connects external experience of the world to a deep, internal sense of self.* When I read this, I knew I had been shown the reason why people write books.

*

Yes, it might sound more poetic or romantic or 'authentic' to expound about the Muse, or inspiration, or desire, but there we're just falling for the bias we hold for crazy creative types again. This is as stupid as it is damaging, but it's almost heresy to dare to say such things in the creative community. You run the risk of being told you're limited, a surgeon and no more than that, and so on. Proof of this has been with us for a very long time; in 1846, Edgar Allan Poe wrote an essay called *The Philosophy of Composition*. In it, he explained (in a very methodical way) the very methodical way that he had written what is today perhaps his best-known work:

his poem, *The Raven*. In the essay, Poe recalls, step by step, how the poem came into being. 'The initial consideration was that of extent,' he begins, and from here, given the poem was for a magazine, he fixes on a length of about one hundred lines.

He wonders next what mood would be most effective for a poem of such a length to be read in such a magazine, and lands upon melancholy. To best convey this sense of melancholy, he fixes upon the notion of a repeated device, a refrain. A single word seems best to Poe. Next, he runs through which vowel sounds could best deliver that sense of melancholy that this refrain needed, and:

'The sound of the refrain being thus determined, it became necessary to select a word embodying this sound, and at the same time in the fullest possible keeping with that melancholy which I had pre-determined as the tone of the poem. In such a search, it would have been absolutely impossible to overlook the word "Nevermore."'

He continues progressively through the entire genesis of the work; and there we have it; The Raven, landed, brought down to earth, or rather to that bust of Pallas at my chamber door. All explained in one short essay.

People hated it. They hated it, or said it was an elaborate joke on Poe's part, that he could not possibly work in this way. That no one does, despite the fact that Poe opens the essay by noting how both Charles Dickens and William Godwin had their mechanical methods. It seemed to actually offend people; probably because we don't want our great artists to work in this way; we want to believe in muses and angels. And moving out to some of the greatest writers I have read about – from Mann to du Maurier – they all not only trusted their own minds more than the Muse, they worked extremely long hours too.

*

Yet, for those who like the romantic view of writing, there remains a little mystery. Yes, I think this is what this little part of the brain, the precuneus, wanted to tell me – from my own experience of writing fifty books, this feels like the authentic version of why a book is made, a story told: something *'out there'*, which is to say external to you, connects with something *deep inside you*. But here's the mysterious part, because finally and absolutely critically, *you are convinced that it means something*. I think it's a very accurate indeed portrayal of the process, and perhaps only this last part contains any delusion. This last part is indeed the true mystery of the whole affair. *Why* does it mean anything? Why should it? But we simply know that it *must*.

Certainly, this seemed to provide evidence for something I had always known; that connections were vital to the creation of books, but also that connections were what got me in trouble in relationships very often. I'd long ago realised that, during those inevitable tricky moments in any relationship, things might be less painful for everyone concerned if my brain weren't remembering and linking to all sorts of other painful experiences at the same time. It only made things worse, and yet I couldn't seem to prevent myself from doing it.

Some of the research into the precuneus steps into even less pleasing territory; it's one thing to make connections, it's another when it verges into a disorder of some kind. Work by Andreas Fink and colleagues at the University of Graz in Austria has shown that this inability to switch off the precuneus is also prevalent in people displaying a trait called schizotypy. Schizotypy is a continuum of personality types that ranges from 'normal' levels of imaginative capabilities and openness to more extreme expressions such as psychosis and magical thinking, as well as higher levels of a thought process called apophenia. The term was coined by Klaus Conrad in 1958 in German as Apohänie, from the Greek *apo* (away from) and *phenia* (to make appear). It describes the way humans can spot patterns in genuinely random data, and is best known in popular thought in relation to spotting the face of Mother Teresa in a Danish pastry, or the face of Hitler in a tea kettle, or the face of whoever in whatever, wherever.

Apophenia is a lot of fun. I'd come across it before, when I wrote a novel about coincidences and how we, in effect, create them through a combination of pattern recognition and cognitive bias – we 'see' what we want to see, what our unconscious is on the alert for. The availability heuristic again. I'd always seen apophenia as an amusing side-effect of sorts to our natural and extremely important human ability to recognise patterns, not something to mark one out as being towards the extreme end of a personality disorder.

Still, all this stuff about the precuneus and the ability to make connections was very interesting, and perhaps is part of why we have come to associate creativity and madness, even if the story has become very muddled in the telling.

Much later, from unconnected reading, I discovered another interesting thing about the precuneus – it is much more active in people who have suffered trauma of some kind. This little snippet seemed to complete the triangle for me, the question of why writers write. Of what they are trying (albeit unconsciously) to do – to remake the world perhaps. As it should have been, as it ought to be. This triangle is composed of the following sides: writing/trauma/healing.

*

I'd found some answers, most of them 'maybe', and some interesting lacunae in our knowledge, proving as always that the more we know, the more we find there is that we don't know. I was reaching the end of everything I thought I could possibly do with this subject, when I came across a news item; the headline referring to research as striking as it was simple: that smart people are more likely to be ill, both mentally and physically.

I looked it up. Published in early 2018, the paper by Karpinski *et al.* is entitled *"High intelligence: A risk factor for psychological and physiological overexcitabilities"*[i] and what they concluded is bad news for anyone who thinks they're intelligent. Or rather, actually is intelligent. Using members of MENSA as a study group, whose IQs fall in the top 2% of the general population, they looked for correlations between high IQ and a range of mental and physical problems. They looked at mood disorders such as depression and bipolar disorder, anxiety disorders such as OCD, as well as Autism and ADHD. For physical matters, they looked at autoimmune conditions, seasonal allergies and asthma.

Putting aside any methodological queries one might have about the self-selection of people who decide they need to/want to/ought to become a member of MENSA, the results were striking. All disorders looked at showed a significant correlation, especially so for mood disorders and anxiety disorders; in the case of the former, over a quarter of the 3,715 respondents in the study had been formally diagnosed with a mood disorder as opposed to around 10% of the general population. For an example of how physical disorders rated, the study group were three times as likely to have a seasonal allergy as the general population: 33% vs 11%.

In order to explain their findings, the researchers proposed what they called the hyper brain/hyper body theory. The argument is that for all its advantages, high IQ carries with it psychological and physiological 'overexcitabilities', or OEs. This is an idea that goes back to work in Poland in the 1960s by Kazimierz Dabrowski, who postulated an OE as an unusually intense reaction to a threat or other stress. More sensitive in every way. If not literally, then to all intents and purposes, more nerve endings than most. Dabrowski's ideas also echo an even older one; the now forgotten Brunonian theory of illness, devised by Dr John

Brown of Edinburgh in the late 18th century, who postulated that all illness was the result of either over- or under-excitability of the organism.

Coming back to the 2018 paper, Karpinksi *et al.* noted:

"It stands to reason that a hyper brain (high IQ), with its overexcitabilities, could be miscommunicating these perceived stressors/threats more often and more intensely than the general population... It has been demonstrated in the literature that an overconnectivity of local brain networks facilitates rumination."[ii]

*

Basically, you're thinking yourself ill. And not just mentally. Their argument is that the two OEs – of hyper brain and hyper body – interact with each other. Someone says something mean to you, you overreact in psychological terms, which in turn causes you to overreact with your physiological responses too, triggering the body's stress response for deeper and longer than in the so-called 'normal' person, thus further endangering physical health.

This research was all fascinating, and reminded me of a gag I've seen in more films than I can recall, a gag based on popular perception no doubt, in which a character is told, 'You're too stupid to be ill'.

*

The obvious next thought was this: if there's a correlation between high IQ and illness, is there also a correlation between high IQ and creativity? And if so, can one then make the connection that creative people are more likely to be ill?

I didn't look into it very far. For some reason, 'Are writers smart?' was not a question I wanted to look at, nor did I think there would be any conclusive research into it. In fact, there is quite a lot of research into the relationship between creativity and intelligence, and while few people would argue that they are exactly the same thing, there is a growing body of opinion which says there is a very large degree of overlap between creativity and intelligence. That they require each other, even if they are not, exactly, each other.

And then, I only had to think about a number of the writers I knew to show that there are big differences between intelligence, and wisdom, or common sense.

*

Why didn't I look into this more? I wasn't really sure; I think maybe I had just had enough for the time being. I think I suspected that all the answers I would find anyway would be 'maybe'. And I think I had started to mistrust the usefulness of intellectual roads, or scientific explanations, for things that were a very long way from being solved, scientifically. It's all interesting stuff to the investigator, and to the researcher, but I was still the sufferer. Given the ball of confusion that was my head, I was only too aware that each new, unproven possibility was doing me more harm than good. At this stage, the number of different explanations I had been given for my chronic fatigue was way into double figures; to give just a few: mitochondrial dysfunction; faulty methylation; chronic, undiscovered infection by one or more of hundreds of possible bacterial, viral, or other agents, such as Lyme Disease, Bartonella, Brucellosis etc. etc; toxic overload; radiation sickness; mould; heavy metal poisoning; adrenal dysfunction; not to mention a vast range of possible psychosomatic causes, if one opened the door to such ideas. Or a combination of two or more of these things. Each new thing that I came across that might possibly be the cause or part of the cause of my illness was just one more thing that multiplied my confusion. The not-knowing had gone off the scale, exponentially. It was paralysing.

*

Instead, I started to wonder if what I should be doing was not learning more about things at all, rather, that I should be unlearning.

The thought had been put into my head by a friend, a psychotherapist, who mentioned in passing one day that much of what people come to him with – matters that they were struggling over – could fall away very easily if only they could unlearn what they know. Or what they think they know. That much of what we need to do in the modern world is unlearn the unhelpful things that we have taken into ourselves, especially the way we think about ourselves. Things that society has taught us, or that our parents taught us, or that in some way we have taught ourselves, but which are damaging us.

My 'gut feeling' was that he was right, and it only took a moment's reflection to see the truth of this. To give just one example, the harm done to women (and men, too) through society's projection of idealised body image; even if not in terms of outright anorexia perhaps, but in a grinding, chronic unhappiness with one's weight. Or body. Or face. Or hair, or skin, or, or, or.... The pursuit of the perfect life we've been told we're entitled to, continually sold to us by adverts and media, without which we should be miserable. That narcissism epidemic that Kristin Neff argues was the unthought-of outcome of the self-worth movement. And so on, and so on.

I started to feel that, maybe, the way to get better was to unlearn some things. Maybe it was true that I had started to learn to be someone else, a sick person, as I had feared. But maybe now I should unlearn my notions of either health, or sickness. Maybe I was helping my body stay ill in my expectations of it; perhaps I was casting the whole thing in the wrong light. Wouldn't it be better to look at what I could still do, rather than what I couldn't? And if that science about overexcitability was right, wouldn't I only help myself by unlearning what I thought I knew about illness, about CFS, about tiredness, and fatigue, and depression? If I just calmed down a little?

*

Easier said than done, perhaps. But it was the summer. The mountains and the forests of the Alps are indescribably beautiful at that time of year. There is a German expression (and this time there actually is, its recorded history goes back at least as far as the 17th century) to describe a state of perfection in life, of all being well: which is that one is living 'wie Gott in Frankreich'. To live *like God in France*. I loved that expression when I first heard it, and after I moved to France, I suspected that the region of France that God would most likely retire to, when it comes time to collect his or her pension, would be the Alps. The streams babble clear and pure; the bells of the cows do not cause fatal attacks of nostalgia as feared, they delight; the skies are blue for week after week; a fluffy white cloud may materialise and then disappear again before your very eyes; the occasional fantastical Straussian storm only serves to remind you of nature's power and how pointless it is to try to worry about our control over it. Or things in general.

Trying not to think about it too much, I took a short walk in the forest, in the very riverbed to be exact, wading through the trickling shallows in bare feet, the sun on my shoulders, leaning on sticks for balance. I became tired, of course, and paid for it later. And in truth, I had walked no further than the maximum I'd been able to since I became ill. What had changed was my attitude towards the walk. Rather than dwelling on the miserable fact that I could only walk a short way, I had finally enjoyed the fact that I could walk at all. And it had been wonderful.

---

[i] https://doi.org/10.1016/j.intell.2017.09.001
[ii] https://www.sciencedirect.com/science/article/pii/S0160289616303324#!

18 – Be Careful What
You Wish For

'Detection of the mutation p.Val617Phe (V617F/G1849T) for the gene coding JAK2,' said the letter. 'The results of this analysis have been transmitted to your doctor.'

*

Four years into the torturous path of chronic illness was taking its toll. So, as the end of the year approached, I made an attempt to see something better coming, no matter what. I'm not really one for New Year's resolutions, but as the new year rolled into sight, I determined to myself that the next year would be an easier one, chronic fatigue or no. I'd be happier; I would try to relax about being ill; I'd learn to cope better with the facts of living with a chronic illness. Things would improve.

Then, on the second day of this bright new year, I got a letter.

*

It came from the hospital down in the valley. I mentioned earlier that there was one last orthodox medical investigation going on in France, something that had been dragging on for ages. My doctor, Dr Mugnier, had decided to send me to a specialist; a doctor called a 'medicine intern' in French. This doesn't mean an intern in the English sense; rather, these are doctors who try to solve problems that other specialists have not been able to; they take a step back, look at a range of issues, do the blood-work all over again.

Dr Loustau was a young woman, intelligent and personable. She'd been pondering over a couple of things in my blood; two borderline scores that many, many doctors had remarked on before but passed over, simply because they were borderline. Dr Loustau nearly had too, but had decided to have one further test performed.

I got the results just two days into the year that I had resolved would be easier. They were positive; I had the mutation of the blood that Dr Loustau had been wondering about. This being the holiday season, I couldn't speak to Dr Loustau, or anyone else at the hospital, for two weeks. In the meantime, I looked up what the mutation with the very long name meant.

It wasn't good.

*

There was bad news, and bad news.

It appeared I had been a borderline case in another way, for a long time, without knowing it. Looking back through the many blood tests I had had over the first years of the illness, it seemed that I consistently scored high for the level of haemoglobin in my blood, with a consequent also high result for haematocrit, which is the ratio of red blood cells to total blood volume. No one had really thought anything about this, because the numbers were right at the top of the 'normal' range, but as I had already learned, what Medicine decides is a normal range for many things can be a matter of opinion, of conjecture. Of 'current best practice'. Just as with the diagnostic checklists of mental health issues so beloved by the DSM, when it comes to physical, more readily measurable factors, the conclusions are often quite as vague. For example, what the United States considers to be a normal range for thyroid hormone levels is different from what the United Kingdom considers normal. No one can seriously suggest that American thyroids are somehow fundamentally different from British ones, so if you're a borderline case, it's a simple lottery as to whether you happen to be living in the States or the United Kingdom as to whether someone will give you medicine for it, or not. If you're even 1% inside the designated 'normal range' for any given matter, it's a rare doctor who will consider taking that particular investigation any further.

Dr Loustau had been that rare doctor. She'd looked at my scores for haemoglobin and haematocrit, and had acted on a hunch. There was a chance, she thought, that these two scores were only so elevated because I lived at an elevated altitude, but when I pointed out I'd only been living up a mountain for a couple of years but that the historic scores had been borderline high, that was enough; she dispatched me to the nurse to give a few more tubes of blood to follow the gallons I'd already given over the years.

The result, a letter, the entire text of which was: *Detection of the mutation p.Val617Phe (V617F/G1849T) for the gene coding JAK2. The results of this analysis have been transmitted to your doctor.*

*

I had become so blasé about test results, and the fact that they never showed anything conclusive, that I nearly hadn't opened this letter. It was the day after New Year; I was at home, trying to get on with the business of existing, even celebrating that existence. The last thing I wanted to think about was being ill and I'd seen the hospital franking on the outside of the envelope. I was within an ace of sliding it into the teetering pile of test results in my study, to moulder with the rest. But I did open it. I read it a few times, which didn't take long, and didn't make anything any clearer with each reading.

I tried to speak to Dr Loustau and was told she'd phone me back in a couple of weeks, when she got back from holiday. So, I waited a day or two, and then I started to research what the mutation with the long name was all about. This time I was not exactly self-diagnosing, as I'd been given the diagnosis. I just didn't know what it meant. The first words I saw said this: 'proceeds inexorably to leukaemia'.

I read what could be found, but it was hard – this mutation is rather rare, and only recently enough discovered that there is little general information about it available to the lay reader. What I came across at first were largely academic papers discussing its diagnosis, prognosis, and so on. It seemed there were a variety of forms that this mutation could emerge as in your body; there was a lot of talk of leukaemia.

Two long weeks dragged by, during which I both tried not to think too much about the fact I might be dying, and not know it, and then, finally, the telephone appointment with Dr Loustau came around. She told me she would have to pass me on to a blood specialist at the hospital, but that I shouldn't worry, not yet at least – she explained that this mutation could indeed emanate in several variants, and that some were not so severe and could be managed.

A couple of weeks after that, I sat in front of Dr B, a haematologist at the same hospital. It didn't go well.

The first bad thing, as explained by Dr B, was that this mutation was not the cause of my fatigue. We had only discovered it, accidentally, because of the continual looking for the cause of my fatigue. I had wanted to find something, and I had indeed finally found something. The trouble was, we had just found a supplementary problem, a bonus illness. Be careful what you wish for.

The second bad thing was that this mutation could be very bad news indeed. Dr B, however, did not seem too interested in discussing it. I tried various questions, but he didn't seem to be in the mood for talking. He was a big man, silent, rather gruff, in French he'd be described as 'comme un ours' – like a bear – quite unlike all the other doctors I'd met in France up to this point, who were without fail amiable and only too happy to explain all they knew about whatever they might be explaining.

I asked if it was serious; Dr B simply nodded and grunted assent. He wrote out a prescription and slid it across the table to me. Dr B explained it was a form of 'micro-chemotherapy' – that it was designed to attack my bone marrow to prevent it from making too many red blood cells, which was the problem. All in all, I was in and out of his office in five minutes. I drove home in a state of mild shock.

All I could feel was the strong sense of (not) irony that in looking for a cause for my fatigue, I had found something possibly worse.

Trying to be practical, it being a long way to drive up onto the mountain where I lived, it seemed a good idea to stop at the pharmacy in town on the way home and pick up the prescribed medicine, shock or not.

'Don't let anyone else touch this,' the pharmacist explained. 'It's strong. A mild form of chemotherapy.'

One thing I had got an answer to before Dr B had whisked me out of his room was how long I would have to take the medicine for; the answer: the rest of my life.

*

I realised that I hadn't actually had the answer to one very important question. In the haematologist's office, I had tried to ask if it were the case that there were three of four possible variants for diseases associated with the mutation known for ease simply as JAK2. Dr B had grunted, but hadn't answered when I asked if we were going to try to find out which one I had. This meant there was a chance I didn't have the most serious case; in fact, it meant I might be taking a powerful medicine for the rest of my life, for no good reason. I read a bit more about the medicine I'd been prescribed; I read about possible side effects, for once. After which, I decided to try to get a second opinion, so I returned to see friendly Dr Mugnier, to ask what he thought.

*

All of this was in French, of course. Though I am far from where I would like to be with the language, I'd understood what Dr B had told me well enough, and yet there's something strange about discussing things in a language in which you are not truly fluent. It's something I had noticed ever since I'd started seeing French doctors about the illness – I could understand entirely the words that someone had said to me, but somehow, they didn't go in. I understood them, but I couldn't feel them. All in all, it often felt as if none of this were actually real. In more general terms, ever since moving to France, I had acknowledged a rather pleasurable sensation of living in a bubble, in a ball of cotton wool. When you live abroad and are not genuinely fluent in a language, you can choose whether to take things in or not – the radio, TV, conversations in public spaces, the news – whatever it might be; you can switch on and listen, or tune it out entirely. I felt a little guilty about it, but equally, I had to admit that I liked it. You can make the world your own creation a bit more, and be less bombarded by the general madness of the modern world. Don't want to know what those people are arguing about on the train? Fine, just turn off.

I also realised, when I first moved to France and made French friends, and so started to have more in-depth conversations than you might have in a restaurant or at the doctor's surgery, that my French had one massive hole in it: I couldn't say bad things about anything. I immediately knew why I didn't have the vocabulary for anger, or disgust, or irritation, or indeed, for almost anything negative; we had simply not been taught such words at school. Thinking back, I could even still see columns of vocabulary written in my textbook or copied into my exercise book; beautiful, pretty, wonderful... There were no words given to us for ugly, angry, foolish, disgusting... and so on. The only negative French word I could remember learning at school was 'triste'. According to my school French, you could be sad, but that was it.

Fans of the much-debated Sapir-Whorf hypothesis – that thought-processes are limited by available word choice – may wonder whether since I didn't have the words for anger or frustration that I was unable to feel them, but I have to disappoint them. I still felt angry and frustrated at how unhelpful Dr B had been, even if I couldn't explain it to Dr Mugnier as easily as I would have liked. Yet there is indeed something about not having the words to denounce someone or something; in the time that one frantically hunts for the piece of vocabulary that you need, you start to question why you really need to express it. Did I really need to tell Dr Mugnier that Dr B was an unfeeling brute? Perhaps, but I'd noted this on more than one occasion, in different circumstances – even the moment's reflection while trying to find something negative to say is enough to allow the very negativity itself to pass from you. Do I really need to say that? No, I often decided, perhaps not. And in doing so, the negative emotion itself would weaken, evaporate.

People, by whom I mean linguists, get really angry on both sides of the Sapir-Whorf argument. I've always thought there has to be something to it, at least, even if the original framing of the hypothesis is now clouded by matters of prejudice and stereotype. As Ludwig Wittgenstein said, "the limits of my language are the limits of my world" – you cannot express something you don't have words for. But that's not to say you cannot *feel*, *see*, or *imagine* something you don't have words for. Dreams prove that point almost every night.

Nevertheless, despite feeling that much of the discussion around my illness was unreal since it was being conducted in

French, I had come up against something serious, and it needed to be discussed, second language or not.

Dr Mugnier was understanding, made a few disparaging remarks about certain specialists, and said I were free to hunt down another haematologist. I liked his honesty: this is not something I know anything about, he said; go and find someone who does. So I did.

*

A few more weeks later, still waiting to find out if I were dying, I found myself in Lyon, in front of Dr Paubelle, a young man who looked like Lionel Messi's geeky twin brother. He was surprised that Dr B had simply dispatched me with strong drugs and no further help; he said he would need to do some tests, since the fact was quite simply that although it was the case that I had the JAK2 mutation, that didn't mean that any forms of possible disease had yet expressed themselves. He'd need some more blood tests, a sonogram done of my stomach, to look for certain symptomatic signs, and the most important test of the three: a biopsy of bone marrow.

The danger with the JAK2 mutation is that your bone marrow starts to overproduce red blood cells. Though that doesn't sound like a bad thing, it is. After a time, your marrow then stops producing red blood cells at all, having seemingly exhausted itself. At which point then, your options in life are – shall we say – limited.

I duly returned for the biopsy a few weeks later. Performed under local anaesthetic, Dr Paubelle had said it was nothing to be scared about, but that it 'would not be the best day of your life.' He was right. It involved taking something like a small apple corer and boring out a chunk of bone and marrow from the back of the pelvic girdle. I'm always convinced that dentists and the like never wait long enough for the anaesthetic to kick in, and I was sure that was the case this time. The nurse had given me the jab, went off to do something while it was supposed to start working, and then came back with the apple corer.

'Ça va?' she said.

'Oui, ça va,' I answered.

'Alors,' she said, 'J'y vais,' and indeed, *in she went* with her implement. It was torture. Still, that wasn't the point. The point was that another couple of weeks later, I sat with Dr Paubelle again as he explained the outcome of all the tests, and once again I was struck by the matter of language, and the effect it had on how I felt about the discussion.

I hadn't asked him to, but he spoke in a mixture of French and English, sometimes even within a single sentence, as he ran through what he'd found.

'Vous êtes dans un 'grey zone',' he said.

A grey zone. Another case of (not) irony. Someone had finally found something wrong with me, been able to diagnose this mutation, but now I was back to the old familiar story. It was impossible to say that I was ill; it was impossible to say that I was not ill. It could not, for now, be determined whether the mutation had expressed itself into a true polycythaemia.

I felt relieved, even if a little guilty, that it was half-happening in English. I felt the words really sink in this time – I felt it. I was in a grey zone.

The only way to accept this result was with the 'no news is good news' affirmation, and so I did. It was a relief. From looking right at the end of life, that end point had receded some way into the unknown again: I was not *inexorably* on the path to leukaemia. At least not yet. But the same can be said of all of us. We are all in a grey zone. We are all undiagnosed, in some way. None of us can say what is coming, not even what may be waiting for us tomorrow. And I was getting used to that at last; getting used to not getting used to it.

What I came away with from this whole episode, which took about eight months of not knowing whether I was about to get cancer of the blood, was this: if I had accepted the first haematologist's consultation as the end of the matter, I would have been dispatched to take a nasty drug I didn't (or don't yet, at least) need for the rest of my life. We are still all brought up to revere doctors and the medical world – it does not seem right to question their authority, and in fact, that very authority is promoted and encouraged by the medical world again and again. It would not do to have every patient question every decision at every step; never mind the burden of time and pressure that that would cause, the truly dangerous thing would be for people to start to learn that doctors are not infallible; that there are many, many aspects of disease that remain unknown; that what one medical system considers to be verified science is utterly discounted in another; that chronic Lyme disease 'exists' in Germany, doesn't in France, and might do in the US or the UK, depending on who you consult; that a score of 25 or more out of 40 makes you a psychopath in Britain, but only 30 or more does in America. Or is it the other way around? I forget now, but isn't that kind of the point? These things are not known, and many, many more things like them. I knew that only too well since I had had my crash course in CME/CFS. If I had been born a hundred years earlier than I had been, I may well have died from tuberculosis, as my grandfather did. If so, I may have been written off as the 'consumptive' type; frail, fragile, little snowflake that I may have been seen to be.

That the medical world needs to keep up the 'we know best' pretence is evidenced by yet another remarkable thing about the placebo effect. There's a thing called the Hawthorne Effect; in which individuals modify their behaviour as a result of being observed. In medicine, this has been seen to express itself as the fact that merely knowing that you will soon see a doctor makes you feel better. Just the thought that someone is going to take care of you has been shown to have a measurable effect on your illness. You may yourself have found yourself in the doctor's waiting room thinking, 'It's so silly I'm here now; I really don't feel that bad anymore'. If so, that was possibly the Hawthorne Effect at work. (Since this is true, I wonder if there is a nocebo version of the Hawthorne Effect for people who have come to dread and fear their trips to the doctor; that they start to feel worse as they approach his or her office.)

Although the placebo effect can still work even if you know it's placebo, it can still work even if you don't believe in it; the more you do believe in the power of your doctor to help you, the better you will feel. Not just feel, the better you will actually be. No wonder 'bedside manner' is so important. No wonder there are papers which show that the quality of the initial relationship between doctor and ME/CFS patient has an effect on their long-term outcome. No wonder Voltaire, who had a lot to say about the medical men of his age, was moved to say, 'The art of being a doctor lies in distracting the patient while nature cures him.'

What if I hadn't gone and got that second opinion? What if I hadn't had the skills to ask for that; nor to even question what I'd been told? Living abroad with less than fluent language is a humbling thing. It often makes you feel inadequate, stupid sometimes. It often makes you feel like a child in the grown-up's world. It's actually quite a good thing, this humility that lack of fluency can impart. But what if I had allowed this to stop me from finding out more about blood mutations, or seeking out Dr Paubelle? What about the thousands of people in a country who don't speak the language well; not just immigrants like me, but poorly educated people, people with learning difficulties? What does medicine have in store for them? Is it a case of simply take-this-drug-and-go-away? And what would happen, on the other hand, if medicine lost its authority?

That was the question that was uppermost in my mind, because I knew that this had happened for me, as an individual, and it had been a brutal awakening. I had spent too long wandering through the wilderness of undiagnosed illness. As the metaphysical poet and cleric John Donne expressed in the *Devotions* he wrote upon becoming ill, and from which the epigraph for this book is taken, the very variable condition of being human can be too much to bear; the simple pain of not knowing. Undiagnosis had destroyed something in me. The simple result was that I no longer believed in medicine.

19 – How (Not) to be a Hypochondriac when You're Actually Ill

'Do you frequently check your body for symptoms such as lumps or bumps, tingling and pain?' asked the website.

Hmm, I thought. That's a tough one. What do you mean by 'frequently'?

The computer screen stared back at me, winning the game of who-blinks-first, as computer screens always do. That is their power; they never give you more than they want to give you.

I tossed a coin, ticked 'no', and went on to the next question.

'Do you avoid television programs about medical matters?'

Hmm, I thought, what exactly do you mean by 'avoid?'

*

I was getting nowhere with this online questionnaire. And anyway, what was I even doing on this website? According to me, I no longer even believed in Medicine.

It sounds like a ludicrous statement, possibly because it is. It didn't happen overnight; I didn't wake up one morning as a medical atheist. It was just slowly knocked out of me, that confidence that doctors know what they're doing, that they can make you better. I suppose I had flip-flopped. Before I was ill, I had never had anything seriously wrong with me, physically at least. I had had severe depression on and off, but had long since stopped believing any therapist or pill was going to magically take that depression away from me. A little bit of gentle running two or three times a week was the thing that had done that, and that route to happiness was now closed. But at least I had never suffered from any major physical illness; just the odd accident here and there, a minor infection or two. For someone whose mother was a nurse, maybe I had had a naïve picture of Medicine: you got ill, you would be made well. That can't be the whole truth; of course I understood that people got terminal, incurable diseases – you can't watch one advertisement break on TV without seeing a charity raising funds for one form of cancer or another. So what I mean is that I, personally, thought that anything I might get could be magically and instantly cured. And certainly, I had not for one second ever thought that I might become ill with something that could not even be diagnosed.

Now that that had happened, and I'd had my crash course in Undiagnosis, I had flipped to another extreme position; I now doubted whether any doctor would ever be able to diagnose, let alone treat, anything else that might go wrong with me. This idea had only been reinforced by the fact that I now 'might or might not' have a polycythaemia. What use was that? We all 'might or might not' have a polycythaemia. Or cancer, or anything, for that matter.

Yet something else had happened, and that was something that had arrived, more or less, overnight. I don't remember exactly when, but one day I realised something – I felt well again.

This is also a ludicrous statement, for I was still ill. I still could not walk for more than a few minutes without problems; I was still tired all the time; my muscles hurt and I was still, generally, exhausted. Yet somehow, at the same time, I felt well inside. Sometimes, I did not think of myself as being ill, at all. Trying to keep that open mind, I wondered if the 'all in your head' gang were right. Maybe I was now well, and was just somehow stopping myself from believing it. So I tried to test it. I tried to go for a short walk on a couple of occasions, keeping the thought that I was ill out of my head, thinking only about the beauty around me.

Five minutes later, and I was dragging myself home again. I was still clearly ill.

But something had shifted in me.

I could feel it, and as I thought about it some more over the next few days and weeks, I decided I hadn't the slightest idea what it meant. Was it a sign that my body was ready to recover? Was it that I was no longer depressed as often? That since my mind felt well, my body ought to, too? Or was it a sign that I had finally accepted the state of illness – that I had finally got used to not getting used to it? The additional suffering from being angry, or frustrated, or scared that you are ill is no insignificant thing, perhaps some of those emotions had started to vanish. I thought about it all, and I couldn't decide which, if any, were true, but the best thing was that I didn't even care, and this was, simply, huge.

The extra burden of worry and fear on top of the physical distress had been great. It had not gone completely; there were still lots of bad days, but I had started to see glimpses of a way of existing that *included* being ill, but was not *only* being ill. I suspect that what is underneath all this is the question of how to be ill, and yet love yourself.

*

At the same time, in recent months, I had started to think more openly about the label which I didn't want to apply to myself; the name at which I had riled so strongly right from the beginning – hypochondriac. It's a pretty awful name; as a society, we find hypochondriacs funny at best, despise them at worst. Pathetic, self-involved individuals who waste doctors' time, time that could be spent helping people who are 'actually' ill. Never mind that hypochondriacs suffer too, in a real sense, even if it were 'all in their head.' Suffering is suffering.

For some reason, I finally thought it was time to take it on the chin – was this really the problem; that I was a hypochondriac?

Never mind the supposed physical symptoms; perhaps I was just creating them through my terrible, self-obsessed nature. I didn't think I was one, but then, hypochondriacs always think only other people are hypochondriacs, right? And I knew a few; people in my own family who think every headache they get means they have a brain tumour, for example, and I knew I wasn't that bad. Still, I needed to look at it. Don't ask me why.

Hypochondria has a long, long history. Its name has changed over the years; today it's usually called *health anxiety* or *illness anxiety disorder* by medical professionals. Originally, the term hypochondria meant something rather different; in anatomy, the *hypochondrium* is the area of the abdomen roughly equivalent to the lower ribs, either side of the thorax. The Ancient Greeks perceived of hypochondria, therefore, as a physically-placed ailment; for Plato, it was the part of the body that desired things like meat and drink and could suffer if not supplied with such. Later, in the Middle Ages, it started to become associated with melancholia in accordance with the then-ubiquitous four humours, or four temperaments, theory. Through the 17th century, this ambiguity developed until finally, in the 19th century, the fantastical nature of the sufferer's ailments came to be emphasised over anything physical. Thus the hypochondriac was born. I decided to see if I was one; did I tick too many boxes in the DSM-5 checklist, for example? What did the available literature on the subject have to say about it all?

According to information from the UK's NHS:

You may be experiencing health anxiety if you worry about your health a lot of the time when there is no medical reason to do this, and how you lead your life is affected by this. You may often seek comfort or reassurance from other people that everything is alright. This may be from family, friends, or your doctor.

You may find you are checking your body for symptoms, and that the more you check, the more you seem to notice strange feelings or lumps in your body.

You may avoid certain activities as if you were ill, and you may avoid anything to do with illness e.g. information or medical programmes on the television.

On the other hand some people with health anxieties find themselves drawn to any information about illnesses and can begin to notice the signs of such illness in themselves.[i]

*

There followed a suitably simplistic, if long, checklist of boxes to tick:

Do you: "Frequently check your body for symptoms such as lumps or bumps, tingling and pain", for example, or "Avoid any information on serious illnesses, e.g. turn the TV off if a hospital programme is on'.

Do you think "I may die if I don't do something" or "Doctors often miss illnesses despite examinations and tests"?

And so on and so on.

I read as much as I could stand; I spoke to my psychotherapist friend: in short, we both agreed I was not a hypochondriac. I 'ticked a few boxes', but so does everyone, more or less.

Hypochondriacs worry excessively about their health for no reason; i.e., when they are not ill. But what if you *are* actually ill? By this time, never mind the questions surrounding Chronic Fatigue, I had also found that I had a blood mutation, something that could potentially be life-threatening. So what does it mean if you worry about your health then, when you are indeed ill? What does that make you? Does it still make you a hypochondriac? Or, on the other hand, would it not actually be crazy to *not* worry about your health if you are indeed sick?

That took some thinking about. But for one thing, that sentence in the NHS leaflet asking if you 'worry about your health a lot of the time' finished *when there is no medical reason to do this.* That seemed to let me off the hook, but maybe things weren't as simple as that. I looked back across the course of my illness and I saw that matters had changed. It was all pretty obvious stuff: it appeared I had been going through all the classic stages that are supposed to apply to bereavement; the famous seven (though some say five) stages of grief: Denial, Anger, Depression, and so on. And here I was, sometimes even managing to see that final stage: Acceptance. Is it wrong to compare chronic illness to bereavement? I don't think so; many people I have spoken to with CFS mourn the loss of who they were, the life they once had, the energy that is no longer theirs to command, as if that version of you has died, and do I even mean 'as if' – can I not literally say that that version of me, the one from 1968 to 2013, is no longer alive? Of course, that's true of all of us all the time – we leave our past selves behind us, every day, and every night, while at the same time, we take those ghosts along with us into the future. Perhaps the difference is just made more marked when there's a neat dividing line – I was well this day, I was ill thereafter, as the quote from Donne which opens this book has it.

*

From time to time, I could see a goal ahead; how to not be a hypochondriac even though I was indeed ill. How to not worry about being sick, despite the fact that I was. It seemed a long way off coming, but it was already true: I had changed in some ways; I had started to learn to be someone else, someone who was ill. Yet I still hated that I was ill, I was still depressed by it, angered by it, and yes, those seven (or five) stages rarely come along in a nice neat order, with no overlaps or relapses. But, above all, I still felt utterly miserable, most of the time, so miserable that I just wished, quite simply, that every night's sleep would be my last. I wish neither to over- or understate this, but I wanted desperately to be dead.

---

i https://web.ntw.nhs.uk/selfhelp/leaflets/Health%20
Anxiety%20A4%202016%20FINAL.pdf

20 – The Chairman of the Bored

'You're bored.'

I've paid for this? I thought. *I've come all the way to London for this idiot to tell me he thinks I'm bored? I got on a plane and melted three cubic metres of Arctic ice and am spending a fortune in a hotel just for this moron to insult me?*

Still, if I had done that, it was my fault because, from time to time, despite the fact that I no longer believed in Medicine, I would still hypocritically follow some clue or another with a doctor. That might sound crazy, but it still seemed worth pursuing possible solutions that I came across, even if I doubted they would work. One example was this trip I'd made to London to see a man who'd written a book about Chronic Fatigue Syndrome/ME. I'd bought it years before, when only recently (un)diagnosed with CFS, but hadn't read it at the time. This was something I felt quite distinctly, even back then – that it was too complicated and probably unhelpful to pursue more than one line of enquiry at any given time. Since I had been slowly following a path of medical investigation from my time in the UK, to moving to France, to the diagnosis of the blood mutation, I had forgotten that I had ever even bought this book. But one day, as I hunted for something in my office, I came across it again. I flipped through it, started to read half-heartedly, but then, as I turned the pages, began to read more eagerly.

One thing that put me off reading the book was this; it was self-published. This isn't because of any snobbery about self-publishing; there's nothing wrong with it in itself. It was just that if someone had truly found the cause and the cure of CFS and related conditions, as the writer claimed, you would hope that a) the whole world knew all about it, and b) that a major publishing house would be only too happy to make millions from selling it. On the other hand, I told myself, I now knew the unspoken truth about orthodox medicine: that it doesn't know as much as it pretends to; that it's often convinced about one thing only to change its mind a few years later; that even major advances can take years to get peer approval and become accepted new method. So, I decided to give the book a try, and within half an hour, I was absorbed by it.

The man who wrote it, who I'll call Dr W even though that Dr is a PhD and not a medical qualification, had had personal experience of CFS. Through his own research and reading, he had come to the conclusion that all the symptoms of CFS were explained by the dysfunction of the chemical pathway between the hypothalamus, the pituitary, and the adrenal gland. So far, that was interesting, but possibly no more than guesswork, but as the book went on, and he began to describe how this dysfunction was expressed symptomatically, I became more and more convinced that he was on to something. It was like that visit to Dr G in Bath all those years before; for only the second time, someone laid out exactly what I was feeling; even down to the weakness in my legs, my problems standing, which no other doctor had ever been able to explain.

One final thing clinched it for me; according to Dr W, the immune system had been sent into permanent overdrive, from constant stress. All the symptoms he described were a result of this, but one thing stood out above all the others: I never get a cold. Ever. What I had had, often, was that weird, drained sensation when you're coming down with a cold, but as Dr G in Bath and I had discussed, it never came to anything. Never an actual cold.

Now, in Dr W's book, he explained that the overload that had happened to your immune system would emanate in one of two ways: either you would easily get infections like the common cold, but not have allergies; or the reverse, where you would likely have allergies, but never get a cold. It seemed I was the second case; I never got colds anymore, and had developed food allergies that I had never had as a child.

It was all circumstantial evidence, of course, but it was good circumstantial evidence; it was convincing. It also gave me hope; for one thing, Dr W assured his readers that you do not need to be scared of your illness anymore; there is nothing seriously physically wrong with you, nothing that can't be reversed. In fact, merely understanding the process that was going on could relieve a lot of the fear and worry. More than that, his book was full of case studies of people making total and almost immediate recoveries. That sounded too good to be true, but it also sounded like something I wanted to at least explore. So I got on a plane to London and went to see him.

*

Dr W worked out of a Harley Street office. I wasn't wild about that – to my mind, it was full of doctors with high fees catering to the rich expat community of London; plastic surgeons, and nutritionists offering 'miracle' diets. But I set that aside as my own bigotry, and turned up at the address he'd give me. It didn't start well; I buzzed the intercom and his voice crackled out at me.

'Marcus?'

'Yes, I'm here.'

'Top floor.'

Top floor. He wasn't kidding. Harley Street is one of the most expensive pieces of real estate in London; old Georgian townhouses; very beautiful but rarely possessing an elevator. This turned out to be the case.

Okay, I thought, it's probably only four floors.

As it turned out, it was seven. Halfway up, I was exhausted and had to stop for a few minutes before going slowly on. I started to wonder about the doctor who cured people suffering from extreme fatigue who had his office on the seventh floor. But I pressed on and made it, out of breath and shaking.

'I got moved,' he said, by way of introduction. He meant his office.

I didn't answer, still out of breath.

'Out of my hands,' he shrugged, unsmiling. I already didn't like him, but I told myself not to be so rash. He might look like the chairman of a second division football club, and he might well be deeply condescending, but he could still have something useful to say. Anyway, I was too tired to go anywhere for a while. I'd paid to sit down for an hour, so I might as well make the most of it. So the consultation began.

To cut it short, Dr W's theory is that there is something in your psyche that is causing your body to rebel. In other words, it's all in your head, but this time, he offered a physical explanation, and a cure – all that you had to do was enter therapy with him, and once you'd found the cause of the problem, your physical symptoms would disappear, instantly, more or less. It was more or less a classic conversion disorder explanation, just with the added element that he was prepared to try to explain the actual physical pathway by which your body manages to let you down, through imperfect action of the hypothalamus-pituitary-adrenal pathway.

In his experience, he said, there were three usual problems: either I was scared, angry, or bored. We talked briefly about my life; I was a writer, I'd fallen ill in Asia, I had had a lot of stress over the last fifteen, in fact maybe twenty, years. Maybe thirty-five. His conclusion? I was bored.

'You live in a house in the mountains. You barely see anyone else. Your work is solitary. You live in your head too much. You're bored.'

238

I tried to point out that I loved where I lived; that I didn't need anyone else. He maybe had a point about being in my head too much, but I liked nothing better than to be alone with a book I was writing; none of it helped.

So then I tried to point out that I had only been living in the Alps for three years, but that I had been ill for five. His reply?

'We can't talk about what was happening five years ago.'

Can't we? I thought. Why not? You seem very happy to make wild guesses about other things...

An hour later, I left, telling Dr W I would consider therapy with him, but already knowing I was not going to take it any further, despite how promising it had all seemed when I'd read his book. Maybe he was right; maybe CFS is caused by a chronically overstressed immune system, and if so, I could do something about investigating that myself. I knew that boredom was not my problem; I recognised the fear and anxiety and anger in my life, yes, but not boredom. I am never, ever bored. As had been the case with Dr G in Bath, I'd had someone seemingly explain the cause of my illness, only to then offer a supposed cure that I simply, deeply felt, was just plain silly.

My session with him reminded me, albeit under a very different guise, of that very first meeting with Dr T. She had made a wild assumption – 'it's all in your head' – and now Dr W had too – 'you're bored', without the slightest rationale behind it. Just guesswork. I wrote to Dr W when I got home, saying that I was grateful for his time, but that I wouldn't take things further, saying that I felt that he wouldn't want to engage in therapy with me, for the simple reason that I was already in another form of therapy. This was true; I had been seeing a woman called Ingrid in the valley at home for some time, and what Ingrid did was proving to be very remarkable.

Dr W wrote back and agreed rather tersely that he would not want to see me if I was seeing someone else, and I was reminded of the Jungian who'd insisted I see her again so she could close that hole in my psyche. It seemed that telling a therapist you didn't want to see them again could be as touchy as breaking up with a partner. Meanwhile, I made a trip every month or so down to the valley, to consult with Ingrid.

I said earlier that I had flip-flopped out of that childish state of thinking that anything medically the matter with me would always be diagnosed and cured, swiftly and simply. And that was the way I was feeling when I first went to see Ingrid, but Ingrid, it turned out, was the keeper of something so powerful that I could not at first believe what was happening.

*

I have merely hinted in this account of being sick how hard it had been, not just for me, but for my family. And yet, finally, I found something that made a little difference.

Ingrid is a psychotherapist practising down in the valley nearby. It's only chance that I found her; long before, Dr Loustau had recommended three approaches to trying to tackle my fatigue. The first was an anti-depressant. That didn't go well; the side effects included a powerful desire to throw myself out of windows and I stopped. The second was a course in a particularly French thing called Balneotherapy, which is rather like very gentle callisthenics in a very warm swimming pool. I found I quite liked it and it got me moving more than I had been, and with the support of the water's buoyancy, wasn't too tiring. The third thing Dr Loustau suggested was a course of hypnotherapy. Yes, the first and third things here meant she felt that some portion of my illness, at the very least, was 'in my head' but I had always had an open mind about that; besides, there was nothing to lose. As with Dr Mugnier, even the way that a potentially 'psychogenique' problem was presented was fundamentally different from the stigma that

I'd felt attached to it right at the start with Drs T and K in Cambridge.

So I duly found a hypnotherapist. I had been hypnotised before, as a young man, when I wasn't coping with the death of my father, and had found it very helpful. At that time, I'd also been surprised to find that it's a surprisingly pleasurable, and deeply relaxing experience. The best way I can explain this is by saying that when you 'wake up' you just feel like the finest version of you.

What I discovered when I visited this new hypnotherapist, about an hour's drive from home, is that I couldn't be hypnotised in a foreign language. Maybe if my French were fluent, it would have worked, but I think the process of micro-translation of her words was just enough to prevent it from happening. I thanked her but didn't return.

Instead, I hunted around, and found Ingrid, and Ingrid, amongst other tools, practises a thing called EMDR. Before I say another word, I'd like to try to establish, even at the risk of 'protesting too much', that I do not hold much faith in apparently miraculous psychotherapies. Over the years, for depression, I had tried many and various forms of treatment, with little or no success. CBT, as I said before, had made some small difference during one part of my life, but I had never found any lasting, significant change; therapy had only ever been a sticking plaster to the wound of depression, never a cure. A friend of mine has found great benefit through Dialectical Behaviour Therapy, but mostly I thought of a succession of friends and acquaintances who just struggled through life, sometimes with therapeutic help, sometimes not.

I also don't want this to be read as proposing that EMDR is some universal panacea, working wonders for everyone. I suspect what is needed in any psychotherapy for it really to be effective is a lot of luck; luck in working with the right therapist, with the right tools, and at the right time. I think that was what happened with Ingrid.

EMDR stands for Eye Movement Desensitization Response, and it has had remarkable success with people suffering from PTSD in particular. I'd come across it because of a now well-known book called *The Body Keeps the Score by* Bessel van der Kolk. It's an astonishing work, now very much better known, detailing years of research and progress into a better understanding of how our body responds to trauma, and the implications for our long-term health.

It's an even more astonishing moment when a technique you really think has to be nonsense shifts something that has been troubling you for years, and does so in a matter of a few minutes. But that is exactly what EMDR can sometimes do, and it's what, amongst Ingrid's other set of tools, it did for me. Things that had been causing me pain for decades, gone in a single session. Things I didn't even know were a big problem until we found out how bad they were, also gone.

One major thing in particular, which I had always dismissed as not being that relevant, or that majorly traumatic, turned out to be a turning point. I won't say what it was; the people involved are still alive. And I didn't even have to tell Ingrid about it, as I had with other issues. This thing was just too shameful, I felt, to vocalise. Instead, I spoke about the way it made me feel, and the emotions of the moment, while we went through the steps of EMDR, which, to simplify, involve visualising and thus, in some way, reliving a moment of trauma, while your eyes follow a series of simple movements.

There is science behind this, as van der Kolk explains in his book, involving the processing of experience during traumatic moments, or rather, the lack of processing. This is not the place to go into details, and I am not advocating EMDR as the cure for all ills. All I can say is that it helped me; it worked like nothing else ever had, and from the moment when Ingrid worked on this large, unspoken thing, everything started to shift. Now I looked at it, I could see how it had coloured everything I thought, and did, and the way I saw relationships. It was a prism affecting, obscuring, twisting my vision; once its power was broken, many other things started to ease and shift. The mere fact that I thought about it often, even though I instantly dismissed it, should probably have told me it was something I needed to address, and even then it was only after a year of visiting Ingrid, once a month or so, that I plucked up the courage to deal with it.

Once I had, everything became a little lighter; a little easier.

I find it hard to write about this because the last thing I want to suggest is that there is always an easy answer to everything. Ingrid was at pains to point out that I – in my turn – did much of the work; that I was ready to do it; that things were ready to change. Ingrid also pointed out all the other ways I had been trying to find an easier way of being: in meditating, counselling, reading, and so on. I also find it hard to write about because it does appear impossible that the simple steps of EMDR could radically change anything, but all I can say is, you have to try it yourself to see. I couldn't believe it was working. This has to be harder, I kept telling myself. But it wasn't hard, it was easy, and it worked. It is a big part of this account of the last five years, even if I am not giving it many words here on the page.

I since found out that two other friends have had EMDR, and with similarly positive results; in one case, the therapist used a stick with a dot on the end as the prompt for my friend's eyes to follow; as she remarked afterwards, it was almost comical how much it felt like someone was merely waving a magic wand over you.

There! You're better now.

And yet it worked.

For her, and for me, and from that point on, things began to lift. If you need more convincing of this, I highly suggest reading

The Body Keeps the Score. It's a book that, having read, you feel everyone should read, or at least have the basics explained. It's as powerful an argument as to why it makes no sense to divide the mind and body that I have come across. Though we long to believe we are free of our past, the famous line by Faulkner says it all: 'The past is never dead. It's not even past.' The cumulation of events and experiences throughout your life, very often from childhood, have shaped you, and will continue to do so until you do two things. First, you have to become aware of what they are, and second, you have to find a way to release yourself from their power.

I looked at this idea long and hard. And I came to a conclusion: the main experience that had been exerting power over me for the last five years had been a curse, a spell of bad magic, shaping my mind, my thoughts, a spell cast upon me with just four, short, simple words.

21 – At War with The Mystics?

'All in your head.'

Four words.

Or to put it in context, 'What would you say, if I told you this is all in your head?'

That was where it all began. Those fourteen words uttered by Dr T were what set me off along the particular path of the journey of my illness. Of course, I was ill anyway, and would have remained so whether she'd said those words or not, but the way in which I have had to carry my illness was, I believe, profoundly altered in that moment. Perhaps it was just the last four words that were what hit home. All in your head. All in your head. From there to today I can trace the flavour of the last seven years of my life, and unless I make a real effort, through it I see its future.

*

Of course, it's not quite so simple. The nature of any biographical piece of writing is that things are streamlined; this book is no exception. I have necessarily had to re-order, re-cast, pull focus and so on in order to try to make something coherent to read. Once it leaves my hands, it will undergo editorial changes, and all these things move us from 'what actually happened' towards something different: a story *about* what actually happened.

The danger of this is that there may seem to have been more logic about things than there actually was; that the stages of development of my illness and more importantly my reaction to it came in discrete steps, nice and orderly. Of course, this book is not how it happened, not exactly. Even if you could remember everything exactly, or had made daily notes, if you were to set things down precisely, a very messy, complicated, unreadable book would be the result. The fact that we do not remember with 100% accuracy has been shown to be vital to our sanity, to our ability to function. That was something I'd read about when I wrote that novel which was the first I'd managed after becoming ill. It's about a man with a totally perfect memory, very loosely inspired based by the 'incredible true story', as they like to blurb, of Solomon Shereshevsky. Shereshevsky was a Russian living in the early 20th century; he was studied by psychologist Alexander Luria for over twenty years, at the end of which time Luria concluded that he had found *no limits* to his subject's memory. What might sound like a blessing was in fact a curse; Shereshevsky lived a difficult and bewildered life. It appears it is simply too much to bear the impact of everything that's ever happened to you, every action, every thought. Obviously, you need a certain level of memory to function as a conscious being, but too much and you are hamstrung by overwhelming data. You need to be able to forget; as the French philosopher Michel Foucault noted, sanity is a balance between memory and forgetting, and not just for the individual, but for society too.

So in writing a book of this nature, all I can do is set this out: that life had become very confusing, even more than normal, and people don't like confusion. It's the main reason that stories exist at all; the attempt to try to make sense out of chaos; it's why stories have to have a certain form for us to respond to them; it's why reading someone's literal diaries can be frequently very interesting but only occasionally *satisfying*. It's why, when they make that 'true story' into a film, and it's a story you happen to know quite a bit about, that you might complain how things have been altered, re-arranged and generally changed. It's why, outside of art, we even try to find the narrative in sport – commentators are keen to explain the backstory that makes the on-field endeavours more poetic; the most satisfying football matches are the ones that seem to complete some kind of story.

There's danger in even pointing this out. In drawing attention to the fact that this book is not a story, and should not be read as a narrative, there's a risk of breaking any power it might have by discussing the issue at all. It's like seeing the puppets' strings, or glimpsing into the wings from your theatre seat – the illusion can be broken. But for reasons I will come to in the next and final chapter of this book, it absolutely has to be said, and so, though I have attempted to write something that is logical and readable; the lived experience of it had very little logic and as unreadable as it was unliveable. As real lives; we just stumble and bumble along, sometimes in a more controlled way, sometimes less; we remember some things, we forget others, sometimes deliberately so. So perhaps even the narrative that drives this book - all in your head - is in itself a fiction, another simple fancy formed from a more complex truth.

Yet if it is a fiction, it is my fiction. It is my narrative.

*

In an extraordinary book published in the 90s, Arthur W Frank discusses the way we narrativize our lives when we become ill. *The Wounded Storyteller* examines the different forms such narratives might take; why we make them, the effects they can have, both good and bad. As he writes: 'a published narrative of an illness is not the illness itself.'ⁱ I have yet to perceive clearly all the subplots of my narrative, but one thing I now believe: being told my illness was all in my head has done me enormous damage.

As I mentioned earlier, according to one researcher I spoke to in preparing this book, around 50% of all visits to the doctor result in the thing I call Undiagnosis. That is to say, half the of time a doctor is unable to say what is wrong with the person sitting before them. It's not something I had ever thought about before I became ill, but if I had, I think I might have guessed at a figure of one in ten, something of that order. But no. Who knew that fully half of the time, our doctors do not know what ails us? Why don't we know this? Perhaps because our doctors would not want us to know this, perhaps even more because we ourselves would not want to know this, must not know this.

As I said before, who else do those of us who live in modern secular western society hold in more esteem, more awe, than our doctors? Unless you are religious and trust your priest, who do we place the most expectation in, who are we the most honest and open with, excluding our families, perhaps even *including* our families? Who do we need the most in times of crisis? Yes, there are times in our life when we might need a lawyer, or a mortician, but they are generally rare. Who is the figure who we most revere, the one we turn to, and turn to with hope and at times desperation, in the lowest and abject moments of our life, the moments of illness? Who else but our doctor? And so then, if, in that very moment of fear that we turn to them and no one else for help, they reject our plea, the result is something traumatic. According to one expert on chronic illness I spoke to, Dr Veronique Mead, the result of the moment when you realise that your doctor is not 'on your side', working with you to find the problem and the solution, but rather is viewing you yourself as the problem, is not akin to trauma. It *is* trauma. It meets the clinical criteria for a traumatic event. It is this that underpins the research that shows that the way you are initially treated by your primary care practitioner can adversely affect the severity and duration of chronic fatigue syndrome; but this does not mean that chronic fatigue syndrome is 'all in your head', it merely means that stress can make it worse.

*

Over the years, I have often wondered what, exactly, Dr T meant by 'all in your head'. I wonder if she herself knew; in researching both this book, and my own illness, I've learned how little training family doctors get in psychosomatic medicine, or psychology in general. Like Dr Mugnier, she may have thought she was doing her best for me. I genuinely believe she was, no matter how damaging those four words. I would have liked to have known. I wanted, after all these years, to simply talk to her about it. So I wrote to her.

It took less than a minute on the internet to find that she had qualified as a GP, and is now practicing at a surgery in the UK. I wrote her a letter in which I very briefly reintroduced myself, told her I was still ill, and wondered if she would talk to me about the experience of being a GP faced with people presenting with something as tiresome and undiagnosable as ME/CFS. I made pains to point out I had no agenda to grind with her, and I don't. (In truth, I was angry with her for a long time, but I'm not any longer; I just see her as an inexperienced, unqualified doctor making ill-informed guesses because she hadn't been given the tools to do any better.) I kept the letter short and polite. I would truly have liked to have had her voice in this book. She didn't write back.

As I said, I genuinely believe she was doing her best for me. She may well have also thought, like Dr Mugnier, that she had reasons to make her guess, but guess is what it was. As Diane O'Leary so powerfully pointed out; there is no logic at all behind the jump from 'we don't know what's wrong with you' to 'it's all in your head'. No logic, no rationality, no scholarship. No morality. No kindness. It is, upon inspection, a vile and damaging guess, based on poor science, perhaps not based in science at all.

'What would you say if I told you this is all in your head?'

As I've said, the only moment in my life, that I can remember, when I said exactly what I should have said, in the moment.

'I would say that you're doing the wrong tests. Or that the ones you are doing aren't good enough.'

And as I've said, Dr T did not like that reply, for it showed that I doubted the power of the god of whom she was the emissary, the mystic; that I was a nonbeliever of her religion – the religion of medicine. At this point, I want to make it very, very clear that in calling medicine a religion, I am not placing myself in the camp of 'anti-science'. I not casting doubt on the entire world of scientific knowledge, like a flat earth believer. I am pointing out that we need to find a new honesty between ourselves, as patients, and the world of Medicine.

The history of Medicine is the story of the movement from ignorance and superstition to knowledge and skill. Take almost any disease and study its history; whether we're looking at tuberculosis, or cancer, or epilepsy; we find the same story of prejudice borne of ignorance finally giving way to treatment based in real understanding. The fact that 50% of all visits to the doctor result in a lack of explanation should maybe not surprise us. Perhaps we ought to be impressed that the figure is as high as that – perhaps we are slowly crawling our way to the point where that figure is 80%, 90%. And if we think about it, how many times do you go to the doctor only for them to say; wait a few days or weeks and come back to me if it's still troubling you. Or, take an aspirin and see what happens? How many times would you guess you have been given a placebo, not even really to try to 'cure' you, but simply in order *for time to pass*? As Voltaire said over 250 years ago, the art of medicine lies in amusing the patient while nature cures the disease. Things have clearly changed, but maybe just not as much as we all like to think.

*

In the 1950s, the sociologist Talcott Parsons described his theory of the 'sick role' which sought to describe an unwritten contract you agree upon when you fall ill in modern (Western) society. In brief, he outlined the rights and obligations of a patient. They were as follows:

- Rights:
  - The sick person is exempt from normal social roles.
  - The sick person is not responsible for their condition.
  - The sick person has right to be taken care of.
- Obligations:
  - The sick person should try to get well.
  - The sick person should seek technically competent help and cooperate with the medical professional.

His ideas have been criticised, but if, as I was, you were never aware that such roles, for doctor and patient, even exist, then any sociological model for examining what is expected of us when we become sick is eye-opening. And one of the unwritten rules we operate under in Western society is to hand power to the doctor when we become ill. We stop being a fully embodied human being with responsibility for ourselves, and instead subjugate ourselves to the keeper of (medical) knowledge. In return, they will make us well. That's the deal. Then we can return to being an active and useful member of society. But this is an ideal, an ideal that works for certain illnesses, less so for others, not at all for some. For chronic, undiagnosed illnesses, it barely works at all. You may embark on the journey expecting to fulfil the rights and obligations of the sick role; but very rapidly it all unravels. In chronic, undiagnosed illness, *no one* knows what they are supposed to do. There are no signposts. Neither doctor nor patient knows how to behave; the textbooks didn't say what to do in this horribly awkward case, other than this: *tell them it's all in their head.* It's cheaper that way, as we've seen. A smaller burden on the health system overall. Not only that, in the US at least, some doctors get paid less if they don't come up with a diagnosis for their patient. They get paid less if they admit they don't know what's wrong. [ii] This is stupid, wrong, and ethically vacant. In the UK, NHS GPs aren't paid for the number of hours they consult with patients. They are paid £150 per patient per year. Multiple that figure by the number of people on their books and that's how much they earn as a base; whether someone comes to see them not one single time in a year, five times, or fifty. As Dr Wendy-Jane Walton, a retired GP, explained to me, this mitigates against giving each patient the care they need, and favours the urge of a GP to minimise how many times they see a given patient. For someone with an unexplained, chronic health concern, this is problematic.

*

This is still the story now, but it is always changing. The story of each individual disease is always changing; the concept of diathesis applied to the tubercular patient; that there was something about the 'type' of person who was more prone to succumbing to consumption, was finally wiped away when the existence and route of transmission of *mycobacterium tuberculosis* was established. No doctor today would suggest you get TB because of your personality; yet those thoughts still sometimes linger around cancer patients. Even stomach ulcers, something that until very recently were believed to clearly be caused by the wrong attitude of the mind – ie stress – have now been shown to be the result of the presence of a bacterium in the digestive tract – *campylobacter pylori*.

So to ME/CFS and a whole raft of other unexplained illnesses. It's my bad luck, and that of an estimated 24 million people worldwide, that I happen to be ill with this disease in the phase before it is understood. But things are changing, all the time, and for one, thing, it's now clear that this disease is a complex multi-system physiological disease, and not 'all in your head'.

How can I finally make such a simple and bold claim for something that has seemed up to this point to be so impenetrable? I do, if nothing else, because of a finding that has now been reproduced independently and verifiably in several labs around the world. The first to demonstrate this effect were Dr Oystein Fluge and Professor Olaf Melia, in 2016,[iii] who showed that adding blood serum taken from CFS patients to healthy muscle cells caused these healthy cells to produce more lactate and require more oxygen than control cells bathed in 'normal' blood serum. There is apparently something in the blood of CFS patients that causes muscles to tire more quickly than in a healthy person. This experiment, performed inside a machine, is clearly removed from any thought processes of the CFS sufferer, and has been replicated many times. At the most extremely cynical interpretation, it would require that CFS patients are able to change the biology of their blood through these thoughts that are 'all in their heads' and thus are the root cause of their illness. There is no evidence as yet that this is possible.

Personally, I have been much taken with the research of Dr Robert Naviaux, of UCSD, who believes ME/CFS, and a plethora of other misunderstood illnesses, to be the result of something he calls Cell Danger Response. This CDR is the result of repeated, chronic stressors upon the body, stressors which can be either mental or physical. It could be psychological trauma, it could be exposure to toxins; the result in his theory is the body reacts with a third option other than the 'fight or flight' response known in times of stress – it responds by 'freezing', effectively entering a state of waking hibernation as a last ditch attempt to manage the situation. What appeals to me about his work is that it is some of the only work which unifies body and mind as a single organism responding to a 'stressor' - in the very broadest sense of the word – with illness. As Dr Naviaux is at constant pains to point out; this does not mean that CFS, or other similar illnesses are all in the head, are psychological in nature. Multiple studies have now shown, for example, a clear relationship between traumatising childhood events, and chronic illness later in life, sometimes decades later. As Bessel van der Kolk argues; the body keeps the score; and we cannot injure either body or mind without damaging the other. I think back on all the trauma (and yes, that is the accurate word) of childhood – of being powerless in abusive situations – and I wonder how much my physiology was changed as a result, how much predisposition to later chronic illness was developed. I won't ever know, but I understand that the process is there.

*

Thing are changing all the time with ME/CFS. I cannot fault the doctor who knows no differently, having not been given that training; but I can fault the still prevailing attitude of 'we always know best', I can fault the attitude that denies the lived experience of the sufferer of a disease. So when I told my doctor that I knew that I was unable to exercise, because I had the lived experience of my body as witness, and was nevertheless told I should 'train' my way back to fitness, to follow the PACE trial protocol of Graded Exercise Therapy anyway, well, I wonder how close to misconduct that falls. Given that at the time I was given this advice, following NICE guidelines, the legitimacy of the research was already being called into question raises the ugly spectre of systemic, health industry-wide malpractice. Given that the PACE trial has now been utterly discredited according to everyone but the people who ran it, and yet the UK's NHS has only now after years dropped GET and Cognitive Behavioural Therapy as the treatments for CFS, does this not leave CFS patients with the right to be very, very angry indeed?

As I mentioned in Chapter Two, there is a war now fomenting between the official views of CFS in the UK, and that of the US, for America has finally come to the conclusion that ME/CFS is a physiological illness, not a psychological one, not even a bio-psychological one. As Diane O'Leary told me, what is at stake is not just the status of ME/CFS, what is at stake is the very validity of psychosomatic medicine itself, because CFS is the pre-eminent disease upon which psychosomatic medicine has set out its stall. O'Leary explained to me in an interview how the field of psychosomatic medicine is a small one within Medicine itself; how a small number of scientists within the camp rule the roost; that papers are generally peer-reviewed from within this circle, and that the results of these papers are then handed down to the general world of practicing medicine with little or no challenge. It is not an edifying picture, and it stands more clearly than any example I can think of as the state that more and more people find themselves in; of being at war with the mystics.

*

I feel for doctors. How must it be not to know everything that you wish to know about your world, your work? How must it be to come face to face with people with 'medically unexplained symptoms' and not know what to do? And then, given the major change of society in the last twenty years, how must it be to see such people try to figure things out by themselves, using the knowledge now available on the internet. For this is the thing that is finally going to drive a wedge between doctor and patient, and perhaps irrevocably, if we do not achieve a new relationship between the two. As Susie Molloy in Snowflake told me, once you become ill with something that medicine does not yet understand, you have to become your own doctor.

I see that for myself, as thousands of chronically sick patients do, who keep abreast of the latest research into their illness, research that may yet take years to become accepted fact, or lead to understanding, never mind cures. As I write, to give one example, new research suggests that ME/CFS may be unique as an illness that responds negatively to attempts to exercise. But will your GP know this if you become ill with it tomorrow and go to them for help? No, they probably won't, and so, despite all the authentic and vital caveats and warnings about the dangers of self-diagnosis, it is foolish to try to prevent people from finding out what is wrong with them on their own, having moved beyond a doctor's care. For the medical profession now to scorn the internet-self-diagnoser, as it often does, is for Canute to try to command the tide to retreat. To try to deny that *sometimes* a patient can work out what's happening better or at least as well as a doctor is unwise; it only drives the wedge further in. And it doesn't have to mean we are denying the skills of the doctor, or her or his years of training. It acknowledges things as they are; that we are a very long way yet from understanding every illness in the world, and that in the face of that; it would be better to work together, rather than in opposition.

*

Speaking of opposition, one of the saddest things to me since I left 'the army of the upright', to use Virginia Woolf's phrase, and entered the world of the recumbent is another war; that between various groups of sufferers of CFS themselves. On social media (where else?) I stumbled across fights, long angry rants, and minor spats, between those who think CFS is caused by X, and those who think it's caused by Y. Those who fight for Z. I've seen fights of the 'you're not really sick' nature, or 'I'm more ill than you are', or 'you can't have really had ME if you got better again'. I mentioned the work of Dr Robert Naviaux above; work that Dr Veronique Mead, herself a sufferer of ME/CFS, catalogues on her blog.[iv] Time and again on the site she emphasises that this work into the long-term effects of childhood trauma doesn't mean that your current illness is all in your head, and yet she is constantly attacked by other members of the society of the suffering for reporting this research.

It has been utterly unedifying watching these disputes, and yes we might understand that they all come out of a place of not-knowing, and of fear, but you would think that people suffering from the same awful problem would pull together, not find individual battles over which to pull each other part. I suppose this proves that age-old aspect of human nature; that whatever area or field or subject we're talking about, people inside it find a way to sub-divide, sub-divide, and find an opposition view to rail against. You see it all the time – within political parties, within the fan base for a football team, or a rock band. I just supposed it would be different with people truly suffering from something awful. This has been one of the most depressing things I've come across during my illness, and as a result I've advised ill people not to be cautious about how much time they spend using anti-social media, for the very reason that it promotes discord. Only to be shouted down, of course.

*

That is one war, but it is perhaps not as dangerous as the war between the sick and the doctor. Can I say dangerous? Isn't that rather dramatic? I don't think so, and this is why: this breakdown in trust is working against that ancient Hippocratic oath of the physician: *do no harm*. For this collapse of trust between patient and doctor is doing harm, in multiple ways. Bad science like the PACE trial and the subsequent policy of GET are harming ME/CFS patients directly. And on the other hand, no doubt, many sufferers have turned away from their doctor's advice, and are following utterly untrialled protocols and treatments, at their own risk, perhaps, but at an *unknown* risk. We must find a new way of relating to our doctors. As the anti-vaxxer movement has shown us; the result of a breakdown in trust between ourselves and medical scientists is that children are now dying of diseases like measles that we until very recently felt had been effectively eradicated. It hardly needs to be said that the arrival in the world of vaccines that may be the only way out of the long-term grip of the pandemic will propel the anti-vaxxer movement even more into the spotlight. At the time of writing, a survey here in France reported that fully 60% of the French do not intend to have the vaccinations. Perhaps it's because they remember some other words of their compatriot, Voltaire: 'A doctor is someone who puts drugs of which he knows little into a body of which he knows less.' Perhaps it's just an innate French resistance to authority, but 60% is, to be blunt, a lot. And it may be extreme, but the numbers who feel the same are growing in many countries.

This isn't just a battle of honour or professional pride. This isn't a question of feeling outraged by a doctor's insinuations, or being disappointed by a health service. Whatever you may know or not know about diseases like ME/CFS, can you think of patients of a single other physical health problem, that some doctors actually *laugh* about? But this is the picture for those conditions that medicine has taken to calling MUS – Medically Unexplained Symptoms – there are multiple threads on Reddit where certain doctors post malicious comments about and laugh at people like me. The relationship between ourselves and our doctors is in crisis, and the potential outcome of this failing relationship is the difference between life and death itself.

---

[i] Arthur W Frank, *The Wounded Storyteller*, Chicago University Press, Chicago, 1995, p22.

[ii] This told to me by Dr Diane O'Leary

[iii] https://mecfsresearchreview.me/2019/04/25/something-in-the-blood/

[iv] chronicillnesstraumastudies.com

22 – The Magic Wand

Before we go any further – there is no magical ending to my illness. Despite Ingrid's magic wand, there has been little change to my life. Not physically. I am still ill: my legs are still weak; I cannot stand or walk for very long; general fatigue overwhelms me often. I have muscle pain almost constantly. As I edit this chapter, I have just emerged from being in bed for three weeks. There are even worse times when the thing people call brain fog descends and I cannot think of the word I want, or mix up two words in a sentence, or two syllables in a word. My typing has gone to pieces; everything takes twice or three times as long as it did before. What is wrong with me largely remains as mystifying as it was seven years ago, perhaps even more so, as I have over the years read dozens of articles and papers proposing the mechanisms behind ME/CFS. Generally, I am convinced by Dr Naviaux's Cell Danger Response hypothesis. But maybe he's wrong, and maybe it's really something to do with the vagus nerve. Or no, it's gut dysbiosis. But wait, here's a series of studies showing the link between Giardia infection and CFS years later; Lyme disease tests are notoriously bad, perhaps it's that, after all; mitochondrial dysfunction must be the heart of it; vaccinations; no, no, you have to consider methylation; and what about that adrenal overload? And so on and so on and so on. Perhaps none of these things are the true cause of my illness; perhaps more than one of them is. This used to overwhelm me. It no longer does, all the time.

*

In the section above, I write *my* illness. I've done it more than once in this book. It's not something I like, but it's something I've noted in myself, and in other chronically ill people. It's not the way you speak about it to start with. To start with, the illness is an invader; the illness is Other. But slowly, as the months and years go by, 'I am sick' transforms into 'my illness' – in other words, like a prison sentence, you end up owning it, whether you want to or not. Sometimes, I consider the relationship of language and sickness, the role that language has to play in the exchange of ideas between 'you' and 'your illness'. I see all these things as part of the way you tell yourself the story of your illness; which is not the illness itself.

I still agree with Virginia Woolf that we do not have adequate language to discuss being ill. I wonder how much better we would understand illness if we did. Perhaps we would stigmatise people with certain illnesses less if we did. Perhaps we could use language in a way that would end the divide between the body and the mind, and that would be a good thing, for this division is helping no one. Ultimately, no disease can be considered to be 'all in the mind', any more than it would make sense to say an illness is 'all in the body'. Thinking about the episode of PNE from which I suffered, the cause of the problem was undoubtedly fear, yet the response was physical. But I believe it simply doesn't make sense to say the 'fear' was in the mind and the 'pain' in the body. They are both in both. Pain only means something because the mind registers it; the fear was experienced not just by my mind, but by the muscles of the pelvic floor.

In all cases of sickness, the whole organism is involved. If we had a better language of sickness we would, for one thing, have a good term for the inextricable unity of body and mind. Is there such a term? In *The Wounded Storyteller*, Arthur W Frank created the term *body-self*. I think a simpler term would be this: person. Perhaps the Buddhist term *nāmarūpa* is probably right. We're all just waiting to realise that Buddhists have been right about it all, all along, anyway.

*

And I also wonder sometimes about apparently small things, such as whether it's helpful or not in any way to use the possessive pronoun 'my' in connection to sickness. Or I wonder why we use the verb 'to fall' in connection with certain things in life; 'fall ill', 'fall pregnant', 'fall in love'. Many are the same in French: 'tomber malade', 'tomber enceinte', 'tomber amoureux'. Why? Is it because all these things are deemed accidental, as when we trip over the raised edge of a paving stone, out of our control?

I wonder about such things, just as I sometimes still wonder what is wrong with me. I still (sometimes) obsess about these things; I am still tormented by them, weighed down, and depressed by them, and so now I know that little has changed in me, after all. I am, perhaps, a touch happier. Not all the time, not universally, not consistently. There are still many, many times when I fall to pieces.

*

I have reached a few weakly-held conclusions about the matters I wanted to investigate. Are writers sicker than most people? Perhaps if they are 'intelligent' writers, whatever we mean by that, according to the study that showed high IQ has been linked to greater physical and mental illness. Is my disease all in my head? I have decided that the question is as stupid as it is meaningless as it is pejorative and damaging. Have I found anything that makes me any better? No.

But overall, I am perhaps a little calmer than I have been in years, and certainly since I became sick.

I think the work with Ingrid was a part of it, perhaps a large part. Perhaps it was other things too. Woolf once wrote that six months in bed had taught her a lot about the thing we call 'oneself'; perhaps seven years of sickness taught me something, after all. Or perhaps I had just, as Hans Castorp so unwittingly but so wittily mused, finally *got used to not getting used to it*. In another weighty novel about TB sanatoria, probably the best-known English language book on the subject, A E Ellis' *The Rack*, protagonist Paul Davenant is told by his doctor, "Consider yourself an experiment of the gods in what a man can endure". Or, as Dostoevsky wrote in *The House of the Dead*, "Man is a creature that can get accustomed to anything." Perhaps all it takes to get used to anything is to stay alive for long enough for that transformation to occur. Perhaps it *was* just the passing of time, but if this were a story, there would be a trigger; an identifiable, even if subtle, cause and effect. There would be a catalyst to this change, and the protagonist would have their big, or small, revelatory moment, after which they become someone new; they overcome their obstacles; they get what they want, or need. In short, unless we're reading a tragedy, they win. And that epiphany is what gets them there.

It's one of the major challenges of modern fiction as to how to avoid cliché in this process; how to deliver the sense of achievement or change that we were following our protagonist for in the first place. One approach to this in modern literary fiction has been to avoid the whole matter altogether. It seems so crass, so heavy-handed, so obvious, to deliver the reader this moment of revelation; or so goes the thinking. The story is dead, so the nihilistic argument goes; it's been done to death in fact, through over-familiarity. As writers, we have to move on and 'make it new', as was the demand of the modernists who tried to sound the death knell for 'traditional' storytelling from the 1920s onwards. I certainly understand the urge as a writer, as an artist of any kind, to want to seek the new and push things forward. But readers do not change so fast, if ever, and nor should they; the reason we invented stories in the first place has not changed; we are still just seeking meaning where (perhaps, or even probably) none exists. That's why so many modern stories that have tried to avoid the cliché of epiphany, of self-revelation are, simply, unsatisfying. Yes, they may be full of admirable prose, and characters who draw you in, and reference all sorts of suitable or trendy or important things, but without that moment of meaning, it all feels dry, academic, lifeless, even if it's more 'true to life' that there is no meaning to the story. For this is where people confuse the notion of reality in fiction with genuine reality. It is *all* fantasy.

Fiction is called fiction for a reason; nothing in it is actually real. Not the dialogue, not the way things fall out, not the clarity, or simplicity, even of the most complex texts. Life is just not like fiction. Yet the best fiction creates an illusion of reality, because it means something to us. It should also be said that the best fiction still finds a way to deliver this meaning, this satisfaction, without just throwing its hands up in frustration at the difficulty of it. *The Magic Mountain*, for one, does it beautifully. As I said before, we never really find out whether Hans Castorp is ill or not, nor do we even know his fate as he goes off to fight on the battlefields of the war, where we last catch a glimpse of him. Uncertainty reigns, and yet we have seen him struggle and grow in his own way nonetheless. It's the poignancy of this empathy that gives us the meaning we seek.

*

That sense of meaning is worth thinking about. Earlier, I mentioned the study of the role of the brain area known as the precuneus, that region of the brain involved in so many rather disparate and esoteric functions such as recollection and memory, the integration of information, the affective response to pain, environmental perception, and more. If they're accurate, in those studies I recognised a true description of the way a story is created: thanks to overactivity of the precuneus, something 'out there' in the real world connects with something deep inside us – some deep memory or deep sense of self – and that, critically, this is combined with the strong and urgent feeling that it must mean something. I said that perhaps only this final part contains any delusion; the sense that this connection *has to mean something.*

Maybe it doesn't. Maybe it's just a side-effect of the brain's evolution. Some people have tried to argue that view. Stories are an amusing, accidental by-product of consciousness. I don't agree; personally, I believe there are very few 'side-effects' in evolution, if any at all; any feature an animal possesses is almost certainly there for a reason. Even things that at first sight seem mysterious, evolutionarily speaking – things such as our love of music, or altruism, or grief – have all been argued to have a solid basis in our 'upbringing' as a species. We even now know what the supposedly useless appendix is for (it's to do with those good gut bacteria again, of course). And far from being a random side-effect of evolution, I rank our need and desire and creation and understanding of stories as perhaps one of the single most valuable traits that our species developed. Here I'm not talking about language in general – that language led to writing and that without language or writing, there can be no civilisation. Without language, there can be no way of passing on what each generation has learned to successive ones. Without language, we are animals, only driven by our genetic instincts; with language, and crucially, with the existence of child-rearing, we can 'stand on the shoulders of giants' and so move our total understanding of the world along, step by step, with each generation. Jaron Lanier, who I spoke about in an earlier chapter, has argued that given how intelligent octopi are, they should probably be the dominant species on Earth, and would be were it not for one thing; they do not exhibit neoteny, which is the prolonged retention of immature, foetal characteristics in the young of the species. Newborn octopi are off into the ocean and fending for themselves from birth, whereas human babies are defenceless for years and require near-constant adult care. This might seem like a huge disadvantage to a species, but as before, evolution 'doesn't make mistakes'; that disadvantage is eventually outweighed by something greater, because what the period of child-rearing enables is that we can give our children more than they were born with. We can teach them, and that teaching happens predominantly through language. That language has the capacity to become writing, and with writing we can build civilisations, for it is our way of recording vast amounts of data, more than any single mind could recall.

But I'm not talking about any of this; I'm talking about what stories do for us in the way we try to make sense of the world. I believe our use of stories has played a crucial part in coping with the vast and otherwise overwhelming nature of the world in which we find ourselves. Stories seek to explain through simplification, and simplify through explanation. They are also a perfect way of remembering and passing information on to others. Not always Facts, but Truth, certainly. I think stories are inevitable beyond a certain level of consciousness; they may even be the best definition of what it is to be human, rather than animal.

I begin to go on too long, but the simple point is this, stories give us meaning, and the meaning that we are looking for is merely this: that we understand something about ourselves that we didn't understand before. Further, it should be clearly understood that stories are not real, and therefore are perhaps a form of delusion, but if so, they are a useful delusion. For if they give us meaning, that's useful. But there's a danger here, and this is what years of illness had finally shown me.

As I said right at the start of this book, the parallel to the global sickness that arose in 2019/2020 is obvious. The belief that we control the world, that we are always in charge, that we can always be smarter than our environment, the view of the technological optimists that no matter what mess we get into, we can always build something to get us out of it again – all these things are no more than stories we tell ourselves, and like my own personal story of health, these narratives have taken a battering of late. The way we see ourselves in the world, both as individuals and as a species, is no more than a story. The question is – is our story helping us, or destroying us?

*

This book is not the story of my illness; no story of illness can be a story, for stories make some kind of sense. In being a writer, and being a reader, and being a human in general, we try to make sense, in the way that books and stories have to make sense, and since I became ill, I had been trying to do that with my life. Desperately. I had been seeking explanation through simplification, simplification through explanation, but what if there just is no explanation? Even this book itself is an example; as I wrote it, I wondered how close to the actual truth it could ever be. And if so, I wondered what the point of it might be, what's the meaning for anyone who might read it, and what can be taken away? What is this journey all about? Where is the revelation, the epiphany? Cliché or not, we need one. I needed one.

But there wasn't one. There isn't one. For illness is *not a story*; illness does not make sense, or only rarely.

'I am ill because...'

If you can complete that sentence, perhaps your own experience of illness makes a little sense.

'I got better because...'

If you can complete that one, too, your own experience of illness perhaps makes even more sense.

But with a chronic and undiagnosed illness, what we have is not sense, what we have is chaos, and chaos is the very opposite of story. Even to try to tell this story of illness, we fail, because the notion of a 'chaotic story' is an oxymoron; it is simply not possible.

Yet (not) ironically, though perhaps a little paradoxically, the failure of trying to find meaning in my illness is itself the answer to that failure. Exactly. They are one and the same thing. The lack of a revelation in this account of illness is *itself* the revelation. The lack of an ending is the ending. I just had to see that.

I had to see that there is no meaning, especially not here, in the recounting of the story of what happened to me when I got sick. This book itself can have no more resolution than the fact that it cannot have a resolution.

*

For those of us that spend our lives in books and stories, it can be very hard to step outside of their power. Why would we even want to? It is an entirely natural, human thing to want stories — stories in the broadest sense of the word — and to use them to find meaning in our lives. We try to turn our lives into a story. We want that story to have a happy ending; we do everything we can to give it one. This is how we cope with life; how stories literally come to compose our lived experience, and very often, they work. My story involved me being a writer who had worked hard, who'd suffered some shit in the early days of life, who was determined, angry, fragile, sensitive, jealous, who would always rise back up but never truly be happy, and so on. When these stories work, we don't see through the cracks, we ignore the inconsistencies. What becoming ill finally forced me to understand is that my narratives no longer worked. I had to start living without trying to turn my life into a story, that is to say, without trying to give it meaning. That desire, that desperate need to find meaning, was awful. It drove me to depression, it tormented me, it weighed me down; it possessed me until there was no room for anything else — not for love, or joy, or ease of any kind. For a book lover to admit that stories might not always be beneficial took some getting my head around; and yet that realisation has in itself been beneficial, as I learned the hard way to let go of my narrative, of my guiding story, of my definition of who I am. Or try to, at least.

I am not alone in this view. The modern French philosopher André Comte-Sponville writes about how his view of literature changed as he got older. As an adolescent, he read fiction voraciously, believing it contained all the truths of the world, but there came a time when he stopped reading novels, for he realised that they were lies. He does not dismiss literature entirely; he only asks that we see it for what it is: a part of life and not life itself.

'I have better things to do,' he writes, 'better ways to live. The most urgent, is to cease lying to oneself. True life is not literature: true life is a life that's true.'[i]

All this, he says, puts literature in its place, which is to say, not the first and not the last.

'Books are worth only as much as they teach us love,' he says, and I wholeheartedly agree.[ii]

*

The whole point of books, especially ones like this concerning someone's 'real life' struggles, is that they have a point, or help you see something, or take you somewhere. Memoirs, especially memoirs of health, are often of the 'I struggled greatly but I came through in the end' variety. How the indomitable human spirit overcame the obstacle. In *The Wounded Storyteller,* Arthur W Frank terms these 'restitution narratives' – put simply, they are stories of *recovery,* and these are the stories that society generally wants to hear about illness. How inspiring! we cry. And maybe we even literally cry a tear or two over the poor, brave and noble soul who made it through despite everything, and then go and start to cook dinner.

But what of other stories? What of stories that do not inspire? What, therefore, of the impossibility of the 'chaos story' – the story where there is no revelation, no epiphany, no enlightenment? No recovery. This is the true story of chronic, undiagnosed illness, and as a rule, most people do not want to hear these stories, for it is the destiny of the 'chaos story' to puncture the happy delusions of the narratives of recovery. 'Chaos story' is an oxymoron, for good reason; we want the stories that make sense, and the story of chronic illness is not that beast. It is not the story of plucky survival of, nor even the tragic, moving, stoic death from cancer, for example. It is the unsatisfying non-story of neither dying, nor truly living, but of being trapped somewhere, in a limbo, between the two. Few people know this story; almost no one is ready to hear it. As sickly F. Scott Fitzgerald said, "There are always those to whom all self-revelation is contemptible, unless it ends with a noble thanks to the gods for the Unconquerable Soul."

*

With chronic Undiagnosis, the situation is of another kind – what we as society demand, as part of a 'sick role' in these cases, is this: silence. Silence on the part of the sufferer. Here, we are largely obliged by the fact that many people with ME/CFS are physically unable to voice themselves to anyone outside the family. Such is the essential nature of invisible illness. If such people do have a chance to have a wider voice, well, here we admire the stoic; the one who puts up with his or her lot, and bears their chaos and pain with grace. For obvious reasons, that is the story we want to hear, but it is not always true. Not the whole truth. For it ignores the chaos, the pain, the fear – all the things we would rather not have to think about, the things that we never believe might happen – until they happen to us.

Maybe that should have been my duty, my role; to *not* write this book. To keep silent, and play the stoic. And that's because the recovery stories we love only have worth because we silently know of all the people who do not recover, from whatever it might be. Without the people who fail, the story of the people who succeed would have no power, no worth.

So perhaps I should have meekly accepted my mute role as one of the vast suffering bodies of the chronically sick, the enablers of the much, much smaller percentage who get to tell the restitution narrative. Or, if I felt I had to write this book, to end it with a different form of restitution narrative; the one of Zen-like acceptance – 'I didn't get well, but I truly learned to be at peace. The end.' Even though this is not true.

I genuinely wonder if it would have been better just to accept my bad luck at becoming chronically undiagnosed, and shut up, because it's just too frightening for society at large to want to hear, too boring, too difficult. But I didn't, I wrote this book instead, and it is clumsy witness to how my life fell apart through illness.

Arthur W Frank said this:

'One of our most difficult duties as human beings is to listen to the voices of those who suffer. These voices bespeak conditions of embodiment that most of us would rather forget our own vulnerability to. Listening is hard, but is also a fundamental moral act... in listening for the other, we listen for ourselves. The moment of witness in the story crystallizes a mutuality of need, when each is for the other.'[iii]

*

So, then, that can be the only point of this book, that there is *not* always a point. That in order to live more easily with unknown illness, we have to be cautious of this storytelling desire. For everything to end up happily ever after. Note that there is a big difference between this attitude and total nihilism. I'm not suggesting one has to live all evil that comes into one's life; rather I am suggesting one takes an open mind to it; avoids attaching meaning to it. 'I wonder what will happen next' – that's the way.

What will happen next is unknown, but I don't, therefore, have to be afraid of it. I am trying to be free, to move beyond the life-as-narrative. Even the tone in which I wrote this book, I had to think about and then free myself of. I have played with the methods of storytelling; in order to make this book readable I have used story, and as I did so, I have had to question if I was making things make more sense than they really did. Was Ingrid really a turning point? I honestly can't say for sure, even though it feels like it. Am I really any happier now? I don't know I can promise to that. But I do know that, finally, I have to let go of the need to make sense of something that simply will not have sense applied to it. Have I done that yet? Most of the time, maybe.

*

According to my psychotherapist friend, 'How do I live with the Unknown?' is possibly the central question of our times. Perhaps of all times. In the not too distant past, we had rituals to tell us how to behave, and thus very largely how to feel, in any given situation. When burying someone, when nursing someone, when marrying someone. Many of us have believed it was enlightened to move on from such rituals. Perhaps it was, but we replaced them with nothing. We are more free; we are more alone. And we do not have rituals to cope with chronic illness. Not for the sufferer, not for the carer. What we have from society at large is this: 'Please don't tell us about this. Really, it's too much.'

We are more free; we are more alone. That's true for all of us; we're all faced with it. Being ill without explanation is only a crystallisation of the state of Undiagnosis that we all live with, every day, should we choose to confront it. But being ill is not a story; it's real life *trying to become* a story – the very thing I ought to step away from, the very thing we have to detach ourselves from, if we want to rid ourselves of a great deal of pain.

So now I try to see myself as... as what? Well, I try to see myself as little as possible. I try to just be; to do the things I can do. If I think about myself at all, I try to minimize the time I think about myself as a 'sick' person. I try to witness the tiredness and pain in my body, and yet not be it. I try to understand the paradox that

The Magic Mountain made clear to me; that illness simultaneously reinforces the connection, and the separation, between mind and body. I am a person with a sick body; but I am not sickness, itself.

*

I have now spent seven years, like one long endless meditation, focusing on illness and what, if anything, it means. The answer: it 'means' nothing.

And I am still ill. I have not become that Zen master, of infinite patience. Sometimes I still howl at being ill; sometimes, I still mourn the things I've lost – simple things like walking with ease, something I used to take for granted. I still feel my illness is my fault; that it has destroyed me, my life as I knew it.

*

I know I need to minimise the amount of time I try to make my life into a story, and thus try to give it meaning. As a writer and a reader and a lover of books and stories, this is easier said than done. I should add that I am not proposing to stop reading. I hope I will not stop writing, either. I love books, I love reading stories, good ones, even if we know that all they are is the fantastical product of someone else's imagination. Someone else's precuneus at work. That doesn't matter; I love them and want them. I need them. All I'm suggesting is that we should know what their dangerous, seductive power is. That we know why we need this drug.

Above all, I'm suggesting that we know when we are turning our lives into a narrative, which is to say – probably all the time. We just need to be aware of what the narrative is. And to know, that for as much joy and wisdom as we might find in a great novel, we should perhaps find time for balance, find time to look out of the window occasionally and think: I really don't know what any of this means, but that's okay. That's okay. I know what has to be done.

i André Comte-Sponville, *L'Amour La Solitude*, Editions Albin Michel, 2000, p88, my translation.

ii André Comte-Sponville, *L'Amour La Solitude*, Editions Albin Michel, 2000, p87, my translation.

iii Arthur W Frank, *The Wounded Storyteller*, p.25.

23 – The Chapter No One Was Expecting

The chapter title is perhaps not strictly true. There were some people expecting this chapter; in fact, there was a small group of epidemiologists actively predicting this chapter – the chapter in which the world, the whole world, fell sick. They were even predicting how; explaining that we were overdue a global epidemic – nothing less than a pandemic – and that given that the previous major one was a hundred years ago before cheap, worldwide air travel existed and when international trade was a fraction of what it is today, that this time we might find it to be worse.

There had been those 'false alarms' of SARS, Bird Flu, and the like, and although you might not manage to convince the families of someone who died in those outbreaks that they were false alarms, you might have been forgiven for thinking that those epidemiologists were scientists over-concerned with their own field of expertise at best, scaremongers at worst. You might have even been the President of a country who had not long before decided to shut research into epidemics down.

Nevertheless, there were those epidemiologists. They had spoken, no matter how few people had listened. There were also, in more general terms, the scientists of societal collapse, those people who have undertaken to research the whys and hows and whats of human extinction, or near human extinction; and in more general terms still, there was the odd novelist, writing end-of-the-world scenarios.

A member of the first of these two groups, a professor of societal collapse, wrote to me, a member of the second of these two groups. He had read the novel I'd put out at the end of 2019, which deals with as-yet-undiagnosed individual illnesses, like the MCS of the Snowflake community, the global sickness of the planet itself, and tried to draw these two things together; the idea being that what we do to the Earth we do to ourselves; that global and individual sickness are – in fact – one, and that, ultimately, it's the planet that will find a way to survive – with or without us.

The professor from the University of Lausanne had been moved to write to me after reading my novel, and we emailed and chatted on video calls a couple of times, finding it amusing that although he lives only a little more than 25 miles away from me as the raven flies, across the other side of Lake Geneva, we may as well have been speaking across continents, confined as we were by the first lockdown of 2020.

He explained that in French-speaking countries, they have a word for people like him: he is a *collapsologue*; someone who studies the ways in which societies end; the subject of *collapsologie*. For societies *do* end; despite the fact that every civilization that has ever existed has come to an end, the vast majority of them have thought they would be the exception and last forever. We, today, are even more guilty of this than the Mayans, or the Etruscans, or the Hun, or whoever it might be. For one thing, societies like the Maya saw time as cyclical, and saw their place within it presumably with more humility than we do with the modern Western notion of linear, *progressive* time. For another thing, we have the apparent advantage of the study of history. It is at our disposal, but we don't learn from it, we don't see that it is about us, rather that it concerns strange and different people from us who are only interesting in an academic way. And if we do think about history, and reflect on all societies eventually collapsing, we know that we will be different this time, because we are so much more modern, and technologically smart. So optimistic.

There are other entire books to be written about this subject, but the *collapsologue* and I discussed our own views on these matters, agreeing that when we talk about the end of the world, what we really mean, is the end of *our* world, the end of us. I told him how the previous summer, I had been lying on the beach one afternoon at Thonon-les-Bains, just across from his workplace in Lausanne, and thoroughly depressed myself by reading the work of one British 'collapsologist', Jem Bendell, whose concept of 'Deep Adaptation' had become infamous in academic circles for two main reasons. There were those who found his reasoning in this now-notorious paper to be over the top, that his warnings were extreme, and most of all, that he had overstepped the boundaries of normal academic protocol with his use of a personal invective that it is already too late for us to draw back from the brink; that what we have to do now is prepare for 'deep adaptation' to the broken new world ahead of us. And secondly, there were those significant numbers of academics and laypeople who had been so persuaded by his arguments that they had had to receive counselling. For if you think you already know all the ways in which we are already living on the brink of utter collapse, you probably want to multiply your estimate by a factor of ten.

In return, the *collapsologue* asked me about my illness, and about how life was up in the mountains. I explained how my normal existence was barely changed by the pandemic. I've had it easy, I explained. I am fortunate in that I work from home, I said. Normally, I leave the mountain once a week to do groceries. Now I do it once every two weeks and wear a mask. I was making light of it; I told him how I'd asked a neighbour, only the week before, how *he* was finding the end of the world.

'Chouette,' he had replied, with his usual smile, despite the fact that his business was making no money; that instead he was working in the organic grocery store in town, on the front line of potential virus exposure.

Chouette. Super. Terrific.

But the *collapsologue* was not finding the end of the world *chouette*. He was finding it extremely hard. He wrote to me only once more, apologising and saying that he was finding it all too much, impossible to work, to concentrate. And this from a man whose daily life is to study the end of the world.

*

And although my neighbour had made light of it, the virus was already here, so close as we are to Northern Italy. His mother-in-law caught it, very early on, and was extremely ill for weeks; she was one of those tested with a kit that produced a false negative, but it was clear what it was. She'd been in Italy the week before; she had all the symptoms, as textbook as they get with Covid-19; she had been extremely ill. But survived. Others I knew were not so lucky; the mother-in-law of a friend who supplies all the local shops with goat's cheese died one Saturday morning. This morning, as I went to give my usual monthly sample of blood to keep an eye on that pesky mutation, I remarked to the nurse how quiet the infirmary was.

'The serious cases are all dead now,' she said. She sighed with respect. '*C'est comme ça.*'

It wasn't quite *c'est la vie*, but yes, *it's like that*, this end of the world, and we are starting to move to its next phase. And some who were ill can recover and the world can recover and we can all go back to doing what we were doing just five minutes before lockdown. And won't that be just fucking great. Because that linear, progressive, consumerist flow of time must go on.

But wait, is there something else to be at least thought about?

*

It's possible I have mentioned in this book some of the more 'opaque' remarks that people say to you about having ME/CFS. And to add to the 'it's the universe sending you what you need' brigade, I was surprised to come across a new addition to the

278

group, as not one but two different people said to me, 'Maybe the virus will lead to you getting better.'

I was too flabbergasted to take the trouble to specify whether they meant the virus itself, or the results of it, the confinement in some way, but there it was – this global viral pandemic was in some way going to miraculously cure my illness. I said nothing, and I certainly saw no signs of that happening.

In fact, I saw signs that I was getting worse. Both physically and mentally, and especially mentally. Like many people, maybe most people, I was terrified by the virus. I was sick for a few days with odd, though mild symptoms; I'd spent time socially with Étienne's mother-in-law just before she was ill; this thing seemed to be wildly more infectious that anyone gave it credit for. But I was fine: at least, I was back to my normal, averagely-ill version of myself. The same thing happened to many other people in the area, but were we all just imagining it? So many people I spoke to felt they'd had a mild version of it, had had the same symptoms; the lack of smell and taste, the cough and so on. But how many people around the world were pestering their partners with psychosomatic fears?

O-ho! I thought, the (not) irony, the (not) *irony*, if I get told all over again that some new illness is likewise all in my head. And I began to sink into the deepest place of suffering I have ever known. I was afraid of the virus, I was afraid of my own state of health, of that of the planet, and of the stupidity that is inherent in optimism; those people who always think everything is going to be all right; well, I thought, they're probably responsible for more than half the messes the world is in. The ones who don't see the need to stop flying so much, or burning fossil fuels, or wearing masks during pandemics. Whereas pessimists tend to think first, right? They tend to think cautiously. So that story we tell ourselves, not as individuals, but as a species, that we will always prevail? Maybe it's not true. Maybe those nihilistic *collapsologues* have the right story, and we should all be very, *very* afraid. In fact, while optimism is what people need to thrive as individuals, when multiplied up to the level of the first species in history to change the functioning of the planet, as we have in the newly-coined geological era of the Anthropocene, perhaps optimism is the *very thing* that will finally kill us. But there's a story that *absolutely no one* wants.

*

The story of Chronic Fatigue Syndrome, and other related illnesses, is not easily told, as I hope this book has made clear. What is indisputable is that these are illnesses with long and controversial stories behind them, the source of a fierce argument between those who see them as physiological or neurological conditions, and those who see ME/CFS as the quintessential psychosomatic disorder.

So what does any of this have to do with pandemics? Two things: two messages, or perhaps it would be better to say, one message and one warning. First, the message.

As lockdown took hold, I witnessed an understandable if not especially noble outburst on social media from people who are chronically ill, heavily rolling their eyes at 'ableds' complaining about having to be confined to their homes for a few weeks. For people who have been literally housebound for years, this bitter cry of 'welcome to my world' may even seem somewhat vindictive, but it is borne of the years of neglect and frequent psychological abuse aimed at people with ME/CFS. If you don't believe this is a thing, trust me, it's a thing. Online: from doctors on Reddit, to idiots on anti-social media, in the 'real world', from doctors you have turned to for help to your own friends and family.

With ME/CFS, you are left to fend for yourself, no longer able to work, stuck at home almost all the time, perhaps all the time, perhaps even in bed permanently, if your case is severe. The vast majority of people who get ME/CFS do not recover; imagine being on lockdown for the rest of your life. So went the cry from the community of the ill, and it was, as we might expect, ignored outside of the community itself. I know this because I tried, and failed, to pitch a story about this to six national newspapers, all of whom were asking for 'your coronavirus stories'.

People with chronic illness don't have to imagine not being able to work, being stuck at home and so on; they have had a lot of practice at being housebound and, thus, they could actually be useful. They have stories to tell that might even help people for whom all this is shocking and new. They could talk about the ways you keep your sanity; the ways to order a day, the ways to try to put meaning back into your life when you have very possibly been deprived of the thing that gave it meaning for you. They could share these things, and clichés though many of them are, from enjoying what you can still do rather than mourning what you cannot, to learning to appreciate the people you care about anew, to being creative at ways to amuse yourself, and bond with others, often via the net, which is a vital lifeline for many of those who are house- and bedbound. But does anyone want to listen? Or are we still only focussed on those restitution narratives?

*

Then, there's the warning. Though there have been some recent encouraging breakthroughs into ME/CFS going on around the world, most notably in the US, we are still some way from fulling understanding the disease mechanisms fully, let alone being able to treat the condition. One thing that many people agree on, however, is that often what seemed to precipitate the illness was an infection of some kind. This was true in my case; I fell ill with classic signs of infection while in Asia six years ago, and though it was never identified, it left me with the permanent fatigue and other symptoms that frequently compound ME/CFS. Though this is not the route by which all people with ME/CFS become ill, it is a very common story; that infection triggers the condition, which remains permanent even when the original infection has passed. This is why it is vital to learn from the CFS story now, before it is too late. Various viral infections have been studied, and the percentage of cases that lead to chronic illness varies, but look at a disease related to Covid-19: SARS. One study into SARS reported that 87% of victims never fully recovered, including fully 17% who were so ill as to never be able to work again. Globally, it is estimated that SARS infected just 8,000 people.

Of course, no one knows what the percentages of victims who contract a long-term health condition will be, but using the worst-case scenario that has been touted – of 80% of the population contracting Covid19 – the figures are alarming. At even the 5% mark of consequential long-term ill health, this would add over 2.6 million cases of people with ME/CFS to the UK's current community of an estimated 250,000; the same number would be added to the USA's estimated community of between 1 and 2 million sufferers of the disease, with just a 1% conversion rate from acute infection to chronic disease; a disease that already costs the USA between $17bn and $24bn annually.

So here's one small piece of advice from someone who didn't want to become ill, who didn't want to have to learn about a disease that society is generally not greatly interested in. There are numerous studies now that show that the severity of ME/CFS is significantly affected by the way it is treated in its early stages; specifically, trying to push on, to work through it, is the worst thing you can do, and can often turn mild cases into moderate ones; moderate ones into severe ones. If you fall ill after some form of infection, give yourself the maximum possible time that you can to recover from it. The attitude we tend to worship in the modern world – keep on pushing – will not work for you this time;

in fact, it may change your life, putting you on lockdown not just for a few weeks, or months, or even years. But for good.

*

Meanwhile, somewhere on a French Alp, something happened. I cannot tell you how, or why, but something changed in me, and it was this: I stopped being afraid. Not a little bit, not just some of the time, but totally. It is that simple. I was no longer afraid of the world. I was no longer afraid of me. I was no longer afraid of my illness, and I finally saw clearly how afraid I had been of being ill, of not knowing what was going on.

Maybe I had reached bottom, but only a fool thinks they have reached a place where things can't get worse: life is remarkably creative when it comes to finding ways to cause suffering. Perhaps it is enough that I am enough of a fool, and I simply one day believed I *had* reached the bottom. I don't know, but whatever changed, it happened quite fast. I stopped reading the news obsessively, limiting myself to a couple of minutes a day. I stopped engaging in the use of anti-social media so much, the dark side of the internet. I focussed on the good things around me, despite everything.

Maybe I had finally taken to heart some more words of that great thinker of my adoptive country, Voltaire, who said, 'I have decided to be happy, because it's good for your health.'*

I also stopped feeling the need to change the world. Instead, in this dark balance, this tenebration between global health and

---

* He didn't say exactly that, of course; Voltaire's 'quotes' are so often the idealised version of what he actually said. But if the story of what he said is useful, well then, it's useful. His actual words in a letter of 1761 to Abbot Trublet were: 'je me suis mis à être un peu gai, parce qu'on m'a dit que cela est bon pour la santé.' 'I started to be a little cheerful, because I was told it's good for your health.'

individual health, I realised that it is enough to change myself, and allow that to be enough. I stopped being afraid, and with that, a happiness that I have not felt for forty years started to emerge. To explode from out of me, like a blessing.

So did the pandemic make me well? Did it make me *recover*? No, of course not. Absolutely not. That would be absurd. Unless, of course, we want to talk for a while about what we mean by *recover*?

Or did the final, final absolute place of quiet, both literally in terms of how hushed the mountain became during lockdown, and the silent self-contemplation inside the head that surely we all now recognise from confinement, work some mountain magic in me? Perhaps. Perhaps. Perhaps.

As those of us with chronic unexplained illnesses have discovered, sickness makes you confront yourself in a way that you have never had to do before. And it can break the narratives you tell about yourself; the stories that give you meaning, the ones that literally get you out of bed in the morning. I have had to move away from who I was before I became ill. That old life, the one full of activity, of walking in the mountains and running in the lanes, of simply being able to stand for more than a few minutes, is gone. A distant memory, it seems now that it belonged to someone else. In its place, I have built a new narrative; one in which I try to make illness as small as possible, and the joys that I still have as large.

*

And the global narrative? What about that? Those sentences I asked in the last chapter; what happens if we ask one of them again, substituting 'the world' for 'I'?

'Why did the world become sick?'

Do you have an answer to that? Some people say they know why. There are those who say it was caused by man-made action; the lack of bio-diversity we have wrought upon the world. And the local woman I mentioned earlier will tell you that actually it didn't really become sick – it was all a fabrication of the 'world government' to give their 5G mast installers a quiet life. Aside from these small groups, be they wise or insane, most of us cannot answer that question. Would it be better, therefore, to stop trying?

And what about the second question?

'Why did the world recover again?'

And to that, surely we have to first ask *if it has*, and, if so, what we mean by *recover*.

*

My fifty-second birthday fell about a month into the severest period of the first lockdown here in France. As mentioned, the normal quiet on the mountain had descended, or I think it would be better to say *ascended*, into a period of even greater stillness. The silence was near-absolute; the roar of the waterfall below the house and the singing of the birds in the forest were the only sounds. The snows were half-gone, spring arriving; when spring arrives in the Alps, you can almost see the flowers growing, it happens so fast.

The only interruptions to this quiet came from the odd sortie by helicopter of the local gendarmes, come to enforce the laws about being no more than one kilometre from your home, on the lookout for rogue hikers making furtive expeditions into the woods. Life was strange, but beautiful.

It was sunny on my birthday; it almost always is. I drove to the maximum of the permitted one kilometre and had a simple picnic within the hour allotted by the rules of confinement during that time. I had upon me the paper *attestation*, stating a justifiable reason for being outside the home; in this case, for up to one hour's *recreation*, just in case I was paid a spot visit by the police, but I knew I wasn't ready to try to explain that 'recreation' originally meant healing. *Yes, Monsieur Gendarme, I have come to this riverbank to heal.*

I sat gazing at the deep pool of clear water, foaming as it churned down a small cascade. The waters that run off the mountain are never warm; in the spring, they are the meltwaters of snow, and are close to zero centigrade. But the Alps have magical tricks up their sleeves. The sun is a frequent companion; the air is thin, and what sun there is strikes you twice as hard. And I love bathing in rivers. There was no one around. I undressed and plunged into the pool, retreating almost immediately. I waited a few seconds and got my breath back, then waded in again, staying there as long as I could. When I couldn't feel my legs anymore, I emerged and went to sit on my towel on the riverbank, letting the sun dry my skin, delighting in that tingle that cold water bathing brings.

As I sat there, looking somewhat ridiculous, wearing nothing but a pair of sunglasses, a young man suddenly appeared on the bank opposite me. There was a path there I never knew existed, and he was strolling along, carrying a fishing rod and sundry equipment, clearly miles from home, far outside the law of confinement. He was maybe fourteen or so. He hadn't seen me at first, but before I could move, he turned his head.

I raised a hand, and nodded a greeting, a little embarrassed at being caught naked. He nodded back, raising his hand as high as he could while still carrying his fishing gear. Without breaking stride, he smiled, and said something to me. I don't know what. My French is not good enough to lip read, and the sound of his words was carried off by the roar of the cascade into the pool, unheard.

It felt like a blessing.

Afterword – A Year of August

Over a year has passed since I wrote the words that conclude the previous chapter. That was to be the end of the book, but in a way, this is a (non-)story that won't have an end. Even after I die, this story we must witness, of hearing the voices of the side-lined and the ridiculed will go on; it has been going on for millennia and will no doubt continue. I have been one tiny part of it; many others have trod the same path, and sadly, will do so in the future.

But since it took time to find the right publisher for this book, and since the pandemic seemed to slow up the world of publishing in general, more than a year has turned, and for me, it was a particularly striking year; a year in which I started searching for a new place to call home; a process that took eight long months, in which I moved eleven times. But this was not the significant thing. The significant thing was that I changed my name.

*

I have been in an easier period with the illness of late.

If I compare myself to the person I was a year ago – in bed for 90% of the time, getting up only to go to the bathroom, wash, or eat, and often eating in bed anyway – the change is dramatic. I can now function; I can cook for myself; I can work. I can stand for longer periods than before; many secondary symptoms have vanished entirely. My mind is my own again; it does not belong exclusively to the illness. I can even have fun occasionally. As I write, I am fully aware that this recovery could take a step backwards again. It could also be the case that it will speed along and in another year or so, I might find myself 'better'. Totally. There is no way to know for sure, and despite this easier period in which I find myself, it does not alter what this book is: if I were suddenly to turn it into the very thing I have been arguing it must not be – the uplifting account of a dramatic recovery from ME/CFS – then I would be betraying its purpose. Its purpose is to witness those who suffer, and who are belittled or ignored. Its purpose is not to provide hope for those who suffer from this and similar illnesses. There are other books and writers out there who have such a purpose and to anyone who is ill with this illness or similar, I suggest reading some of them. As I said earlier, the purpose of this book is not to tell anyone how to recover from chronic illness; the purpose of this book is to offer a voice to those who do not recover – to say 'you exist', to say 'you deserve to have your story listened to'.

*

So, to return to the fact that I changed my given name, I will try to say why, and what this has to do with this story.

Just over 14 months ago, as I write, a sequence of coincidences occurred to me that was so preposterous that I was forced to pay attention. About ten years ago, I wrote a novel about coincidences. Like many of us, I had been fascinated by them all my life; like many of us, I have always wondered what they 'mean' and why they occur, and so I'd long wanted to write a book that dealt with the subject. In the research for the novel, I came across some of the very many other people who have been similarly obsessed by coincidence – from Arthur Koestler, to George Price, to Wolfgang Pauli, to Carl Jung, who coined his term *synchronicity* to better encapsulate his view of the phenomenon. The fact of the matter is that I – like many, many writers I know – have noticed that coincidences tumble like an avalanche when you are preparing to write a novel. Coincidences around the theme of the book; synchronicities connected to the research; ludicrously serendipitous moments of all kinds just pile up, one upon the other. I used to be rather freaked out by this; later, I came to wonder why it was happening; these days, I simply love and welcome it as one of the most beautiful parts of the beautiful process that is writing a book. I take them to be a sign that the book is progressing well and that I am on the 'right track', whatever that means.

But this time, the series of coincidences that occurred to me were not about a novel I was writing; they were about me. To be precise, they were about my name, the name Marcus.

I do not know your view of what coincidences are – what, if anything, they represent to you – but I tend to think two things. First, that they are the conscious product of the unconscious making connections (and as I noted much earlier, making connections is one of the three keys of writing, along with the imagination and obsession). We humans are evolved to be absolute fiends of pattern recognition – and put simply, given the practically infinite number of things that can coincide with another practically infinite number of things, it would be weirder if coincidences *never* occurred. That would be truly odd. But secondly, I also think that coincidences are not chance. I am really not very sure I believe in free will anymore, given everything I have learned – *through this illness* – about who I am, why I think the way I think, behave the way I behave, and so on. And so, I tend to think that if you are struck by a coincidence, it is by definition because it has meaning *for you*.

So, all this being said, of course I was going to pay attention when this ridiculous series of coincidences about my name happened to me.

To cap it all, one evening, as I sat at home – wondering about this series of synchronicities about the meaning of the name Marcus – I wrote to a friend explaining it all, knowing it would amuse her, and knowing that she had been involved in a part of it, unwittingly. As I pressed send on the email, another email arrived in my inbox, at that very moment. It was from a friend of mine, who I had not spoken to in a few months. I knew she was pregnant, no more. But now she wrote to me as she entered the third term, and said, 'We know it's a boy. We're thinking about names. Actually, we're thinking about the name Marcus – do you know what it means?'

Oh yes, I thought. I know what it means. In that moment, I felt the weight of my name, a name I had always liked. Or so I thought, because now, as I felt it sitting on me, I felt it holding me, pressing me down, making me suffer. For a moment, I wondered what it would be like to take that name off, and in that same second, the narrative voice in my head said this: 'you're called August.'

Ignoring the possibility of incipient madness, (for what is madness anyway?) I decided to pay attention. In my mind, I took off the name 'Marcus' and I tried on the name 'August'. I liked it. I felt lighter, easier, more hopeful.

Over the next few months, I wondered about making the change permanent, not just for a few moments. I realised I would need to keep using the name 'Marcus' for my books, but I saw no reason why I could not become August on a daily basis, for friends, and family, and for me.

So, I did.

*

It was an interesting thing to tell people – seeing who accepted it without batting an eyelid (my daughter loved the idea), and who really struggled. Some French friends told me the name was old-fashioned, pretentious, the name of a clown, in fact. I thought those three things fitted me quite well, and was not deterred. Other people liked the new name but struggled to see why I had changed it; these sometimes being women who had changed their (sur)name when they got married. I couldn't see the difference.

There is power in words; there is power in names. As a writer, I fully believe this. In fact, I believe words and names are very much magical spells. Any writer who doesn't believe that is missing something – a writer can literally change your emotions, your world view, your beliefs, sometimes, using words alone. What else, ultimately, is a magic spell?

So yes, names are important, and maybe that is what, unwittingly, lay underneath some people's difficulty with me taking a new name. So, I tried to explain that it was simply like using a pen name, only in my case, my original name is my pen name, and the new one is the one I use for myself.

But there was one final thing to look into.

One part of the series of coincidences about my name had come about through a French book of the meanings of first names. Naturally, I am a sucker for this stuff – as before, I fully believe in the power of names, the natures of who we are and how we are defined by the collective cultural unconscious surrounding all words, but especially names, the very words that define us. So, when I had read, in this French book, that amongst other things, 'Marcus' was *someone who may suffer from an illness for which medicine has no response*, I had had to listen.

But what of August? What hidden histories lie in his pretentious, old-fashioned, clown of a name? Supposing I changed my name from that of one sick person to another? How would that profit me? So, I checked, and found that yes, Saint August had also had a chronic illness, but that he recovered. He recovered from his malady when he built a chapel.

But what does all this have to do with this story of chronic illness? The answer is: nothing. Nothing much. I have not seen an easing in my illness because I changed my name. That would be an absurdity; even the most devout of the 'All In Your Head' gang couldn't ascribe a miracle cure to this nominative act. Could they? I like the coincidence of August's story, that's all, and it remains to be seen if the improvement in my health continues on the right path.

*

As the year came to a close, and after eight months of moving and living in rented places by the month or just the week, I finally bought a house, a new place to call home. I moved in on a cold, wet day at the end of December. It is now the spring. There is some work to do here; there is a garden, and some land. On the land is an old grange, it is a total ruin. Walls starting to tumble, the roof long gone; trees that must be decades old grow from inside, including the largest and thickest-trunked elder I have ever seen; it leans one weary, snaking branch on a half-fallen wall and I do not know who is supporting who. Perhaps they are supporting each other.

I do not know whether I will achieve that 100% recovery, but I believe I will. There is still work to be done, of course, but I think I can do it. There is still time. Time in which, perhaps, to build a chapel.

Appendix: ME or CFS – What's in a Name?

The answer to that is: a lot, when it comes to the often intense, sometimes vitriolic debate about the very name of the illness I have referred to in this book as ME/CFS.

First of all, let me offer a definition of the disease, from the website me-pedia.

Myalgic encephalomyelitis (ME) is a chronic, inflammatory, physically and neurologically disabling immune mediated disease that presents with symptoms involving multiple bodily systems. It is frequently triggered by a viral infection or a flu-like illness. ME presents with symptoms in the central nervous system (CNS), autonomic nervous system (ANS), immune system, cardiovascular system, endocrine system, digestive system, and musculoskeletal system. It was classified by the World Health Organization (WHO) as a neurological disease in 1969.[i]

*

That is making things about as simple as they can be made, but even in the above, there are disputed issues; for example, you'll note no mention of the term CFS in the above. To explain what's going on, we need to briefly look at the history of the illness to date.

The first *recorded* cases occurred in Los Angeles in 1934 when there was an epidemic outbreak of the disease in the Los Angeles County General Hospital, but it seems probable the disease was occurring prior to this date, but unidentified. If you know a little about ME/CFS, the fact that there have been at least 75 documented *epidemic* outbreaks of the disease may come as a surprise. Most people, if they know anything at all about it, perceive it as a disease that affects individuals, and which is not infectious. Argument still persists about the latter, as does the naming of the disease.

After the LA case, the illness was termed 'atypical polio'. Following outbreaks in Iceland in 1946-7 and 1948-9, it came to be called either "Akureyri disease" (after the town where it occurred) or "Icelandic disease". As mentioned briefly in a footnote in chapter 2, a further epidemic outbreak of the disease at the Royal Free Hospital, London, in 1955, is now infamous in the history of this disease. Briefly known as "Royal Free disease", it was soon found that there were more general, non-epidemic cases in the population at large. The term "benign myalgic encephalomyelitis" emerges around this time.

Myalgic encephalomyelitis was coined as a name by Dr Melvin Ramsay, who wrote a detailed account of the outbreak at the Royal Free, where he was consultant physician in Infectious Diseases. The term describes the contemporary view of the symptoms. Breaking the name down, we have:

Myalgic – painful

encephalo – relating to the brain

-myel – referencing the spinal cord

-itis – meaning inflammation.

*

The Royal Free outbreak is perhaps the moment where we can pinpoint the origin of the belief of the disease as being psychological in nature. In 1970, two psychiatrists, Colin McEvedy and A William Beard, published a study of 15 epidemic cases of 'benign myalgic encephalomyelitis', including that at the Royal Free. Why *psychiatrists* were investigating an outbreak of a disease is something that might have given us pause for thought before they'd even begun. Their conclusion, despite writing at a distance of 15 years and without interviewing a single sufferer, was that the outbreaks were cases of either mass hysteria on the part of the patients,[ii] or "altered medical perception of the community" by doctors and others. In brief, they used the phrase 'psychosocial phenomena' to name the cause of the illness, and their legacy is still with us.[iii]

A 1990 cover story by Newsweek looked at CFS, and though it attributed a biological origin to the illness, it also used the term "yuppie flu", belittling just about everything to do with this life-changing disease, and making a correlation totally unproven with the personality of actual sufferers.

After an outbreak in Lake Tahoe, Nevada, in 1984, the magazine *Hippocrates* ran a cover story, and used the term 'Raggedy-Ann Syndrome', a name which fortunately did not catch on, despite the fact it captured the nature of the muscle weakness which is common. The term chronic Epstein-Barr virus had been in use in the US for some time, but after researchers of the Lake Tahoe cases found no evidence of the presence of EBV, they proposed the name chronic fatigue syndrome.

Just over a decade later, in the UK, a report instigated by the then Chief Medical Officer proposed the term chronic fatigue syndrome as being the most suitably representative name.

Yet this is a name that is not favoured by most sufferers, according to research by the ME Action Network carried out in 2016. The reason for this is that the name CFS has become associated with the 'psychosocial' model of the illness.

The word 'psychosocial', and the term MUS (Medically Unexplained Symptoms), have become very charged in the argument over the nature of the illness, because, under the cover of scientific-sounding terms, they actually are declaring that this disease is 'all in your head'. You might not realise, when you go to your doctor with an unknown ailment, that when the consultation is over, they may have ticked a box on a checklist in your notes, putting your case down as MUS. If you were to find out and learned that MUS means Medically Unexplained Symptoms, you might not think much about it. It seems to be just a neutral expression of the facts – your case cannot be determined – but if you are given this label, you have just been placed in the bucket of being ill for psychosomatic reasons.

This view of the unexplained illness has been spread by influential scientists. One such is Dr Simon Wessely, professor of *psychiatry*, who was appointed director of the Chronic Fatigue Research Unit at King's College London in 1994; his view is that ME/CFS is a "general disorder of perception". Another is Dr Michael Sharpe, who was the lead author of the "Oxford Criteria" for diagnosing CFS – which specifically exclude some of the main physical symptoms of ME, but state that psychological criteria are to be included. Both Wessely and Sharpe have frequently addressed employers' organisations and health insurance groups, making plain that they need to write ME/CFS off as a psychological disorder, to avoid swiftly mounting costs in the face of rapidly rising numbers of people with this chronic illness. Dr Sharpe, for example, has a long involvement with UNUM, a major life, disability and health insurer. UNUM reported that from 1989-1993, claims for disability due to ME/CFS had increased by an average of 460%. In order of insurance costs, ME/CFS came second in a list of the five most costly conditions, three places above AIDS.[iv]

UNUM's "Chronic Fatigue Syndrome Management Plan" describes ME/CFS as *"Neurosis with a new banner"* and the same document states, *"UNUM stands to lose millions if we do not move quickly to address this increasing problem"*. At a UNUM supported symposium on 17th May 1995, where the term "malingerers' charter" was in use, both Dr Sharpe and Dr Wessely spoke, in order to make plain their view that insurers need to cling to the opinion that ME/CFS is a psychological ailment, in order to avoid paying out crippling amounts of money on disability claims. Both these doctors, and many others in positions of influence, are on record as repeatedly stating that ME/CFS is not real.[v] On occasion, they even go so far as to make fun of sufferers. Witness Dr Byron Hyde, a Canadian physician who has made it his life work to study ME/CFS:

'Several years ago, I was lecturing in British Columbia. Dr [Simon] Wessely was speaking and he gave a thoroughly enjoyable lecture on M.E. and CFS. He had the hundreds of staff physicians laughing themselves silly over the invented griefs of the M.E. and CFS patients who, according to Dr. Wessely had no physical illness whatsoever but a lot of misguided imagination. I was appalled at his sheer effectiveness, the amazing control he had over the minds of the staid physicians. [...] His message was very clear and very simple. If I can paraphrase him: "M.E. and CFS are non-existent illnesses with no pathology what-so-ever. There is no reason why they all cannot return to work tomorrow."'[vi]

*

This is a huge issue, and not the prime focus of this book. I have only given here an overview of the reasons why if you are of the opinion that ME/CFS sufferers sometimes seem a little paranoid, it's with good reason. There *are* people, influential, government-appointed people, specifically, clinically, financially trying to tell you that your disease is all in your head.

*

As I mentioned in chapter 2, some people are very insistent on the name they choose to use for this illness, and as sufferers, that is their right.

There are many people who will be upset that I have used the term ME/CFS in this book, because they believe that ME and CFS are two very different things. There are those who dislike the term CFS, but also dislike the term myalgic encephalomyelitis, for the technical reason that (they say) it is not proven that inflammation is a component of the illness, which is what that '-itis' denotes. They have, therefore, proposed the term ME remains, but with 'encephalomyelitis' replaced by 'encephalopathy', denoting not inflammation but rather a disorder in a more general sense, 'pathy' deriving from the Ancient Greek for suffering.

I don't find fault with any of these viewpoints. It's why I prefer the term Undiagnosis, to honestly state that no one has been able to identify what is wrong with me, as with so many other people in my situation, but that that fact cannot be used to declare that my illness is, therefore, purely psychological.

Sufferers are often (with legitimate reason) sensitive about merely the very name of their illness, and this is understandable given the awful nature of psychological and perhaps we might say even *physical* abuse that is sometimes directed towards patients; from doctors on Reddit laughing at their patients, to being told you're imagining that you're ill, to being forced into trying Graded Exercise Therapy, only to have that turn your moderate case of ME/CFS into a severe one, in which you become bedbound for life.

I have only hinted at the issues here, and the controversies surrounding merely what to call this disease. For further reading, I suggest either the comprehensive website me-pedia.org, or *Osler's Web*, a book by Hilary Johnson, journalist and ME/CFS sufferer, who spent the best part of a decade researching the shortcomings of America's health care services with respect to their approach to the disease. For more on the involvement of certain psychiatrists with the disease, and their relationships with the insurance industry, I recommend the website www.margaretwilliams.me

ⁱ https://me-pedia.org/wiki/Myalgic_encephalomyelitis
ⁱⁱ McEvedy, Colin P., and A. W. Beard. "Royal Free Epidemic Of 1955: A Reconsideration." *The British Medical Journal*, vol. 1, no. 5687, 1970, pp. 7–11. *JSTOR*, www.jstor.org/stable/20379056. Accessed 7 Dec. 2020
ⁱⁱⁱ ttps://meassociation.org.uk/2017/05/during-me-awareness-week-we-revisit-the-toxic-legacy-of-mcevedy-and-beard-10-may-2017/
^{iv} http://www.margaretwilliams.me/2003/notes-on-insurance-issue-in-me.pdf
^v http://www.margaretwilliams.me/2017/quotable-quotes-continued.pdf
^{vi} Byron Hyde, *Missed Diagnoses*, lulu.com, 2009

Other books you may be interested in:

Master Your Chronic Pain: A Practical Guide – from pain specialist Dr Nicola Sherlock – adopts a holistic view of pain. Each chapter looks at a different aspect of pain management, from the benefits of mindfulness meditation to overcoming a fear of exercise to strategies for improving sleep. The emotional impact of pain is discussed, and practical tips for managing stress, worry, and low mood are given. Strategies for managing thoughts and emotions are explored, and the impact of pain on relationships is examined.

This book uses principles from Acceptance and Commitment Therapy (ACT) which has – for many people – been established as an effective therapeutic approach in the management of chronic pain.

THE 15-Minute RULE for FORGIVENESS

CAROLINE BUCHANAN

Forgiveness is one of the most powerful and liberating actions a person can take. Whether it is forgiving others, or yourself – for past deeds or mistakes – forgiveness can open people up to a life of happiness, fulfilment, and newfound accomplishment.

And yet, so many people struggle to generate forgiveness. Whether it is a partner who cheated, a friend who dishonoured themselves, or personal guilt that has haunted you for many years – forgiveness is hard! Yet, the power to forgive, and move on with your life, can bring untold rewards and enlightenment.

The 15-Minute Rule is all about creating a safe framework for fostering forgiveness and self-forgiveness. We can all find 15 minutes in our busy lives and, through the short exercises and examples in the book, forgiveness and mental serenity can be attained. In this book, best-selling author Caroline Buchanan shares candid stories from her life, and those of people she has worked with, to create a no-nonsense book, jam-packed with advice and practical instruction so that you can start to develop forgiveness today.

9 781914 066214